D1094135

The Adventures of Ulysses

THE ADVENTURES OF ULYSSES

BY GERALD GOTTLIEB

Illustrated by STEELE SAVAGE

RANDOM HOUSE · NEW YORK

Second Printing

 Published in New York by Random House, Inc., and simultaneously in Toronto, Canada, by Random House of Canada, Limited.
Library of Congress Catalog Card Number: 59-5522
Dewey Decimal Classification: 883
Manufactured in the United States of America

To

Robin

CONTENTS

Foreword

Ulysses lived a very long time ago—twelve centuries before Christ. In the country of Greece men worshipped not one god but many, a whole great family of gods, presided over by Zeus, their father, from his throne high in the clouds on Mount Olympus.

Zeus ruled the heavens and his brother Poseidon ruled the sea. There were many other powerful gods and goddesses, whom men were careful not to anger, for they believed this would bring destruction down upon them. If a man acted fairly and moderately to his fellow men and respected and honored the gods, he had nothing to fear. But if he failed to show the gods proper respect, or if he acted in an uncivilized way toward other men, the vengeance of the gods could be terrible and swift: thunderbolts from mighty Zeus, wild, stormy seas from the Earth-Shaker, Poseidon, and wounds or death in battle from Athena, the war goddess.

The world of these ancient Greeks was dangerous indeed. A man needed courage to live. And even more, he needed to be clever, for he never knew when his life might depend on his outwitting some powerful enemy. Of all the men who managed to survive in those far-off days, one—the hero of this story—became the most famous for his quick, resourceful mind.

Here, then, are the adventures of Ulysses, wiliest of the Greeks.

G. G.

The Adventures of Ulysses

The Boar Hunt

Young Ulysses saw the glint of sunlight on the yellow tusks before he saw the boar. Motionless, the red-haired boy kneeled at the edge of the mountain brook, water trickling from his cupped hands. He watched the boar from the corner of his eye.

The animal was a giant, gray and lean, and its curving tusks looked as sharp as the spear that the lad carried to hunt it with. But now Ulysses was separated from his keen-edged spear by the width of the stream. The weapon stood upright in the opposite bank, where the boy had plunged it a moment ago. Was it just out of twelve-year-old high spirits that Ulysses had vaulted the brook before he knelt to drink? Or had he unwittingly offended some powerful god, who then tricked the boy into exposing himself to this mortal danger?

The danger was coming closer. On sharp hoofs, the muscles rippling in its massive haunches, the gigantic wild boar trotted slowly into the clearing. It stopped a short distance from the kneeling boy. Ulysses had not stirred, although his mind was racing ahead. The gray boar and the wide-shouldered boy in the white tunic eyed each other.

The green clearing on the slopes of Mount Parnassus was deathly quiet—except for the rasping of the boar's heavy breath and, some distance away, the sound of Ulysses' grandfather Autolycus calling to his sons in the mountain woods. The boar hunt today was in honor of young Ulysses, son of King Laertes who ruled over the island kingdom of Ithaca.

But the boar knew nothing of faraway island kingdoms. Nor could it tell that the purple border on the white tunic signified that the boy was of royal blood, and would be king in Ithaca someday. The boar merely snorted, lowered its big head, and prepared to charge.

In the next moment the sunny glade was filled with the snarling, gasping, and thrashing of a fight to the death. With one motion, in the instant before the boar was upon him, Ulysses was clever enough to scoop up a handful of earth and hurl it into the animal's eyes. The boar bellowed with pain, and its charge was deflected. But still it thundered on. Quick-moving Ulysses barely had a chance to spring to his feet before a yellow tusk had ripped into him like a sword blade, gashing his right leg deeply above the knee and sending him sprawling half into the brook.

He rolled to one knee as the maddened boar came roaring at him down the sloping bank, slashing the air with a blood-tipped tusk. This time the boy, thinking fast, whipped his short tunic off over his head and flung it into the animal's snout. Holding a corner of the garment, Ulysses tried to entangle the boar's tusks and drag the charging beast into the shallow water.

But there was a ripping sound as the boar tore wildly at the cloth with its razor-sharp tusks; it would not be dragged down. A final slash swept the tunic away, and the boar lunged on after Ulysses, who was now splashing madly across to the other bank and toward his bronze-tipped spear.

By the time the sputtering, snorting boar had gained the bank, Ulysses was ready for its next charge. Panting, the boar eyed the stream of red blood that trickled down the boy's right leg. Its shaggy flanks heaving, the mighty animal sniffed, and tossed its foam-flecked snout. A shred of white cloth clung to a bloody tusk.

A few steps away, Ulysses slowly, watchfully drew himself erect. Glistening wet with water and blood, his bronzed body was now clad only in a loincloth. Ulysses drew a deep breath and filled his broad chest. Already at the age of twelve he had the powerful shoulders and thick chest of a full-grown man. The red-haired boy gripped his long spear and suddenly spoke.

"I am Ulysses . . ." he said aloud to the boar. He stopped to catch his breath, then spoke again.

"They call me Child of Anger." His voice was clear and young, a boy's voice in an almost-man's body. "Come, try my anger," he said to the panting boar. "Come," said the proud boy Ulysses. His eyes were calm, wary.

"Come, boar," he said, shaking the bronze-tipped spear a little. "Do not be afraid. It is no bad thing to die in battle."

The boar charged suddenly.

"But it is better to live!" cried Ulysses, springing to one side and raising his heavy spear with both arms. The boar was upon him now, swerving its powerful head to hook sideways with its tusks like a farmer cutting the high grass of summer with a sharp sickle. But Ulysses snatched his leg out of reach and brought the glittering spear down with all the force of his thick shoulders and strong-sinewed arms. Through the boar's great haunch he drove the bronze spearhead, past the bone and into the very heart, so that the animal went to its knees in the dust, coughing bright blood, coughing its life out.

In a few moments all was over. The glade was silent again.

"You fought well," said the boy aloud, looking down at the dead beast. "If you were a man I would

Through the boar's haunch he drove the bronze spearhead

strip the armor from you now and carry it home to my treasure house."

"And so you shall with this king of boars!" bellowed a deep voice from behind him. "You shall have his long tusks to carry home with you to Ithaca!"

Ulysses did not turn around, even when he felt a hand on his shoulder. He knew the voice of his grandfather Autolycus.

Then the sons of Autolycus—Ulysses' uncles—came from the forest's edge where they had stood watching the fight. They gathered around the kinglike boy.

"The hunt is over," said the eldest uncle, touching the dead animal with a sandaled foot. "The soul of your brave enemy has gone down to the House of Hades."

He took his nephew by the shoulders and looked into the boy's gray eyes. "When you are a man," he said, "you will send many a warrior of courage down to that place with your spear or your sharp arrows."

Young Ulysses put his hand on the ashen shaft of the spear as it stood up from the body of the huge boar. "Yes," he said slowly, looking down at the pool of blood soaking into the earth, "and may the gods always be as kind to me as this."

"They may be," said his uncle, "if you honor them always, and respect your fellow men."

"Enough!" cried the old and grizzled Autolycus. He threw a long arm about his grandson's shoulders. "Let us bind up our young hero's leg, and I will say a spell I know to stop the bleeding. Then will we hurry home and feast on this brave animal that fought a king's son and lost."

Soon the hunting party was to be seen moving quickly down the mountainside. The crest of lofty Mount Parnassus reached high above them, catching the golden rays of the afternoon sun. And far off, but still in this same land of Greece, the dying sun gave glory to the peak of Mount Olympus, where the gods lived.

War

Ten years passed. One warm day, when the sun shone down strongly on the island of Ithaca, a young man stood on the beach. His arm was about the waist of his wife beside him. They watched their infant son playing happily in the surf.

The young man had red hair and a short, curling red beard. His chest and shoulders were massive, and his arms long and powerful-looking. His legs were rather short for his great torso. On the right leg, just above the knee, was a long white scar.

"Ulysses!" the dark-haired wife said. "Those waves grow too big."

Ulysses strode forward and scooped his son up in one strong hand. He splashed back, holding the child high in the air. The boy screamed with delight.

The mother screamed a mock scream too, as Ulysses dangled the squirming boy over her head. Sparkling drops of sea water sprinkled her face. "Stop!" she cried, laughing. But Ulysses reached out with his free arm and swept her up into the air also. She shrieked, and the boy chuckled gaily, and Ulysses laughed up at them both.

They were so occupied in their happiness that they did not see the messenger approach. "King Ulysses!" he said from behind them.

Ulysses, King of Ithaca, lowered his wife and son gently to the sand. He turned.

"Yes?" He looked down at the messenger, who was a young page from the palace. "What is it, Elpenor?"

The boy bowed deeply to King Ulysses and Queen Penelope. "Sire," he said, "a ship has just come into the harbor, with two kings aboard. They ask to speak with you."

Ulysses bent toward a purple cloak that lay on the sand. "Who are these kings?" he asked.

"Sire, they are King Agamemnon of Mycenae and his brother King Menelaus of Sparta," the boy answered. "They wait in the palace now."

Ulysses swung the cloak over one bronzed shoulder. "Stay here with the Queen," he said, and strode off.

Penelope frowned after him. "What more do you know of this, Elpenor?" she asked. Her eyes were on the broad back of Ulysses as he climbed the hill behind the beach.

Elpenor's face reddened with excitement. "They

say, my lady, that there is to be a war! All Greece is arming to fight the kingdom of Troy!"

"Troy?" demanded Penelope. "Troy is far away in Asia. What quarrel have we with Troy?"

"They say, my lady," said Elpenor, "that a Trojan prince has stolen the wife of King Menelaus."

"Queen Helen?" Penelope said. "She is very beautiful, of course, but . . ."

"A thousand ships, my lady!" said Elpenor. "One of the sailors said a thousand ships will sail to Troy! We will bring back Queen Helen and all the gold in the city besides!"

The burly fist of King Menelaus came crashing down upon the table. "War!" he said to Ulysses. He was a heavy man, dressed in a tawny lion-skin cloak. The two front paws came forward over his shoulders and were held together by a thick gold clasp at his throat.

"War!" he repeated. "Proud Troy has overstepped herself this time. She must be destroyed, or none of our homes and wives will be safe!"

King Agamemnon—tall, hawk-nosed, with black, glittering eyes—put his hand on his brother's shoulder. "Menelaus is right, Ulysses," he said. "King Priam's kingdom grows too powerful, too dangerous. We must break Troy now, before it is too late!" His pointed beard jutted out at Ulysses like a black dagger.

Menelaus spoke again. "All the princes of Greece are coming," he said. "Not a single one has refused."

"Menelaus," said Ulysses slowly, "I know how beautiful your Helen is. And I know I have vowed to fight in any war we Greeks wage, but——" He looked about the great marble hall of his palace. "Can we not get Helen back peacefully?"

Agamemnon shrugged his shoulders and answered for his brother. "Perhaps," he said. "We will try. But meanwhile we raise an army!" He leaned forward. "Ulysses," he said softly, "I know it is hard for you to leave your young wife and your child. But would you like it if some Trojan prince came and carried off Penelope? Troy grows stronger every day. It is now or never!"

He straightened up, and spread his hands out broadly, and smiled. "Besides," he said, "the war will be short. We will crush Troy easily if we strike now with all our force. Come, Ulysses—a quick attack, a short war, and then back home again in no time!"

The two royal brothers waited while Ulysses slowly walked across the marble hall and rested his hand upon a smooth pillar. He looked out the far doorway. Over his shoulder could be seen a peaceful green meadow, and trees dark against a slope beyond. The hall was cool. Young King Ulysses stood gazing out upon his homeland for a long moment. Then he turned and faced his guests.

"You will come?" Menelaus asked.

"Aye," said Ulysses quietly. "I will muster my people and join you."

"Well spoken!" Agamemnon cried, and he stepped forward to grasp Ulysses' hand. "There is more than just glory to be won at Troy," he added. "You know how rich old King Priam is. We will divide his wealth among us!"

Ulysses smiled at this, and then summoned servants and bade them make the royal guests comfortable. He excused himself and went in search of Penelope.

She was still on the beach, watching their little son build a sand castle with Elpenor's help. Ulysses looked at the sunlight gleaming on her long hair as he approached. When she turned toward him he saw the tears glistening on her cheeks.

He dropped to the sand beside her, and clasped her in his arms. "You know about the war?" he asked.

She nodded. And then suddenly she clutched him to her fiercely, digging her fingers into his back. "Do not go, Ulysses!" she sobbed. "Oh, please say you will stay—please, *please!*"

He stroked her shining hair and answered softly, "I have no choice, my love. I have pledged my word." He lifted her chin and looked into her dark, tear-filled eyes. He said, "Would you have me sit quietly at home when every warrior in Greece is arming for battle?"

Penelope sat up and brushed her hair back with both hands. Her fingers trembled. She tried to smile, but failed.

"You may be killed," she said.

"I cannot hang back because of that," Ulysses answered. "It is my duty to go."

She began to sob once more. "My darling," Ulysses said, stroking her white cheek, "there is nothing to worry about. We go against Troy with a thousand ships. Think of it—a thousand! It will be a short war. I will be back here with you and little Telemachus before you know I am gone."

Penelope said nothing. Ulysses turned and looked at the two boys playing in the sand.

"What do you build there, Elpenor?" he called.

The boy answered, "We build Troy, sire!" And he lifted the child Telemachus up in his two arms, above the castle of sand.

"Is it not so, Prince Telemachus?" he asked. "Isn't this the fortress of King Priam?"

Little Telemachus squirmed and kicked. His bare foot struck a battlement of sand, and crumbled it. He kicked out again and knocked down a whole wall.

Elpenor laughed, and so did Ulysses. Telemachus chuckled gleefully and kicked again at the sand castle, and then even Penelope laughed.

"You see?" said Ulysses. "The walls of Troy are weak. It is a good omen. The war will be short!"

But the war was not short at all. The mighty Greek fleet assembled, and sailed far across the sparkling sea to Asia, and laid siege to the citadel of Troy—but the walls were not made of sand after all, and they did not crumble. Row on row of slim black Greek war vessels lay beached on the shore below Troy. They lay there for ten years.

There were fierce, bloody battles, and at first it seemed that the Greeks might triumph quickly. But help poured into Troy from all along the Asian coast. The fighting went this way and that, and would not end.

"Well, it is time the war ended, one way or another," Menelaus said. They were sitting about Agamemnon's campfire, which blazed in the black, moonless Trojan night. Not far away, at the sea's edge, the dark shapes of war vessels were silhouetted against a line of white-gleaming foam. Up from the shore, at the beginning of the plain that stretched toward the citadel of Troy, a ragged line of fires crackled and flared. The figures of many men could be seen moving about in the light of the flames.

"I wonder what the Trojans think tonight," said Agamemnon, "when they see us breaking camp at last, and burning our tents." He turned his hawklike face to look at the circle of Greek chieftains around the fire, and he smiled broadly, as though at some joke.

Ulysses leaned forward to warm his hands at the fire. "Why," he said, "they will think they have won the war, will they not?"

The other chieftains laughed, and Diomedes, who was King of Argos, said, "You are wise, Ulysses," and they all laughed again.

Agamemnon said, "Let us drink to the wise Ulysses!" He clapped his hands sharply, and a servant darted to his side. "Wine!" commanded King Agamemnon.

"Let us drink," said Ulysses, "but not to me. We should drink to the father of the gods, Zeus the Thunderer."

A murmur of agreement ran about the fire. Ulysses took a two-handled drinking cup, heavy with gold and jewels, and held it toward the wine-bearer. The servant first poured in water, and then added the strong dark wine.

All the Greek chieftains watched respectfully as the pious Ulysses poured some of the sweet-smelling wine on the earth as an offering to the all-powerful gods.

"In the name of almighty Zeus, the father of gods and men," said Ulysses in a ringing voice. He put the goblet to his lips and drank. And all around the fire the flickering light glinted on raised wine cups.

Beyond the little group of noblemen about King Agamemnon's campfire could be heard the busy sounds of the Greek soldiers as they dismantled their camp and prepared to sail away from windy Troy. Bronze armor rang and wagon wheels creaked and whips snapped over the backs of straining oxen. The burning tents crackled away in the night.

Some distance up from the shore, a fiery line marked the great stockade the Greeks had built to protect their camp during the ten-year siege of Troy.

At the far edge of the plain beyond, the black bulk of Troy's high walls rose up.

There was a loud laugh from Diomedes. He wiped his mouth with the back of a broad hand and said something to young Prince Neoptolemus beside him, and laughed again. They both looked up in the darkness—not toward Troy, but at a large shape closer by, just beyond the burning stockade.

Ulysses followed their eyes. The strange, huge form loomed up in the blackness like some giant animal, the height of many men. It stood there, solid and unmoving, in the dark night that lay upon the plains of Troy. What was it?

Ulysses smiled.

"It is time the war ended," Menelaus said

Welcome to Troy!

"They're gone! They're gone! The Greeks are gone!"

The news was quickly abroad in Troy. It was morning; people came out of their houses when they heard the happy shouting, and stood blinking in the bright sunshine. Then they ran to the gates of the city.

The soldiers allowed them to climb up to the parapets and look out at the empty plain, but they were a little afraid to leave the protection of Troy's massive walls. After ten long years of war the long-suffering people of Troy could not quite believe that the fierce Greeks had gone. Some of the Trojan children had never been outside the walls at all; the Greeks, about whom their parents told them frightening stories, had been besieging the city for as long as they could remember.

Could the siege really be ended now? Had the

Trojans won the long war after all? Were the terrible Greeks really gone?

"A beautiful day for the end of the war—if it *is* the end," said a Trojan to his friend as they stood elbow to elbow in the crowd at the western wall. They laughed together nervously and looked around at the surging mass of people. All of Troy would soon be crowding up to the high ramparts of stone. Were the Greeks really gone?

"The King!" someone shouted; and old King Priam, in gold-embroidered purple robes, and a tall purple hat like the headdress of the goddess Athena, came walking slowly and majestically through the crowd. Tall soldiers of his palace guard cleared the way for him, their bright helmets flashing and their bronze-tipped spears held high.

Priam looked grave, and a little sad. He had lost more than one well-loved son in ten years of battle with the furious Greeks. But then what parent in Troy had not? It had been a bitter, bloody, tragic war.

The old king came to the foot of the square-cornered watchtower that flanked the proud Scaean Gate. The breeze stirred his white hair as he turned to face the anxious people of Troy. He gazed imperiously at his subjects for a long moment. The crowd stirred, murmured, then fell quiet. Only the sighing wind could be heard, blowing in from the sea.

Suddenly Priam, king of the Trojans, raised his hands high above his head. The wide purple sleeves fell back from his thin arms, pale in the sunlight. He shouted just one word.

"Yes!"

There was a moment of silence. Then a wild roar burst from the crowd, and laughing, screaming, dancing, singing, the people of Troy surged out of the gate and into the empty plain for the first time in ten years.

On the beach beyond the plain they discovered the Horse. It was so big they wondered why they had not seen it from the walls of the city, three miles off. Made of wood, painted bright yellow with a black mane, it towered high above the sandy beach, mysterious and awesome, its black eyes staring. Why had the Greeks left it? the Trojans asked themselves uneasily. They milled around the broad base of the huge effigy, rapping the strong wood with their knuckles, squinting up along the curving sides, and wondering.

Besides the Horse, the Greeks had left nothing. Where there had been a stockade of tightly set tree trunks protecting their camp, there was now only a long line of fire-blackened stumps. Instead of the massed Greek tents, with rows of many-colored pennants fluttering from their proud tops, now there were only charred rags on the yellow sand. And the hated Greek ships, long and black, with red-painted prows, were no longer drawn up on the Trojan beach. The warlike Greeks had truly gone, and there was no sign of them anywhere on the sparkling sea.

But why had they left the great Horse of wood? What did it mean?

"It is a peace offering!" shouted a Trojan soldier, brandishing his spear. He wore a plumed helmet and a breastplate of gleaming bronze. "The Greeks have lost the war and are fearful that the gods have stopped smiling upon them."

"Why stand here talking?" growled a swarthy archer from Phrygia, his curved bow slung at his back and a spotted leopard-skin about his bare shoulders. "Let us take it back to the city and celebrate."

"Back to the city!" shouted a young warrior from Thrace, and the word leaped through the eager crowd like a spark in a field of sun-dried straw.

"Back to the city!"

So the joyous Trojans scrambled about the base of the bright-colored animal of wood, shouting and singing, mad with delight after all their weary years of war. Shouting and singing, they hauled the giant Horse to Troy.

When they had pushed and dragged their prize up to the city's massive wall, in front of the Scaean Gate, the people of Troy paused. A white-clad figure, with dark hair streaming in the wind, stood atop the square watchtower. It was Cassandra, the unhappy daughter of King Priam. Princess Cassandra was a dark-souled girl who kept herself aloof and brooded much. Many thought her mad; some said she possessed the gift of seeing into the future. Now Cassandra stood with her arms crossed on her breast and her eyes flashing in the bright sunlight.

"Trojans!" she called out in her wild voice, high above them on the tower of stone. "Trojans, do not destroy yourselves!"

Cassandra, lordly Priam's troubled daughter, pointed at the Horse, whose black and lifeless eyes stared back at her.

"Burn this evil thing!" she cried. "Burn it!"

But poor Cassandra's words were lost, blown away by the mocking sea wind. The Trojans drew the Horse through the gate and into their beloved city.

And then the day was given over to gleeful dancing and singing and wild revelry. It was a happy time for Troy. The war was over.

The cold moonlight gleamed on the white stones of King Priam's palace. Within, everyone slept. Throughout all of happy Troy the people were exhausted from the long day's celebration. The only sound was the flapping of a pennant in the wind that never stopped blowing across Troy from the sea.

The Horse stood in the darkness of the palace courtyard. A single shaft of moonlight lay along its curving flank. All was still in the courtyard of Priam's great palace, except for an occasional snore from a sleeping reveler sprawled blissfully on the ground.

Suddenly the stillness was broken by a creaking sound, like that of a door being swung open on stiff hinges of leather. Silence again. Then a slight noise; and from the broad underbelly of the Horse a thick rope abruptly fell. It hung twisting and turning in the half-light, its end reaching almost to the ground.

The rope had been dropped from a trap door in the Horse's body, and now a pair of legs came into view as a man began to lower himself quickly down the rope, hand over hand. The legs came swiftly toward the ground, and the pale moonlight fell upon them. Above the right knee glistened a long scar.

Ulysses was all warrior now. A polished helmet covered his red hair, and he wore the full armor of battle, from carved breastplate to bronze greaves. He dropped lightly to the ground and darted into the shadow against one of the massive legs of the Horse. His razor-edged sword gleamed in his hand as he scanned the sleeping courtyard.

All was peaceful. Ulysses stepped back toward the swaying rope, sheathed his sword, and looked up.

"Menelaus!" he hissed. "Neoptolemus! Elpenor!"

Down from the hollow Horse came these three, hand over hand, their bronze swords dangling at their sides; and silently after them came more fierce Greeks, armed and wary and thirsting for Trojan blood. Grimly they spread out in the dark courtyard, clutching their murderous weapons.

The drunken reveler still snored happily on the

cobblestones. Prince Neoptolemus, he of the flashing eyes and terrible war cry, stepped over to the sleeping man and cut short a snore with his pitiless dagger.

Agamemnon and Diomedes and the other Greek chieftains waited impatiently in the black shadows outside the Scaean Gate. Behind them their battle-hardened army was drawn up in silence, row on row of grim warriors. Here and there the moonlight glinted on bronze spearheads and polished armor.

There was a clashing of metal and a scraping noise as two chariots brushed together somewhere in the darkness. Diomedes drew in his breath sharply. Had the Trojan sentries heard? The Greek army stirred restlessly, and the chieftains close under the wall looked quickly up at the dark ramparts. But no sentry showed his face over the edge. Troy was fast asleep tonight, from sentry to king.

"This silence pleases me not," grumbled Diomedes to King Agamemnon. "It could be a trap. Might not Ulysses and his men have been discovered and taken prisoner while we were bringing our fleet back here?"

"It is a risk we must face," said Agamemnon. He looked out past the army to the moonlit beach where the Greeks had landed in their black ships, after rowing back silently in the night.

"Ulysses and the others are taking a greater risk, I think," said the tall warrior Diomedes. He ground the sharp butt spike of his heavy spear into the earth.

They spread out in the courtyard, below the Wooden Horse

"Building the hollow horse was the craftiest idea Ulysses ever had," he added, "but I swear by the god Apollo I would not like to be——"

Suddenly a great shout split the night. It came from somewhere inside Troy. Then there was a second shout, followed by a fearsome scream that ended abruptly.

For a moment the warlike chiefs stared at each other in puzzled silence.

"Almighty Zeus!" whispered Diomedes. "What does that mean?"

Agamemnon shot out a long arm and clutched his shoulder.

"Listen!" he hissed.

Somewhere inside the gate there was the sound of clattering footsteps. The Greek chiefs drew back warily into the shadows.

The massive Scaean Gate slowly began to creak open. The Greek soldiers in the front ranks crouched behind their shields; a row of strong-fingered archers dropped to one knee, bows poised. Every Greek held his breath.

It was Ulysses. He stood in the gateway, his naked sword dripping blood. Behind him was young Elpenor, grinning from ear to ear, and beyond the two of them the flames of a great fire could be seen.

Ulysses bowed mockingly to King Agamemnon.

"Welcome to Troy!" he said.

The army gave one hoarse battle cry and then

pelted forward into the open gate. Like hungry tigers on a blood scent, the sharp-weaponed Greeks poured into hapless Troy.

"Not a Trojan man will live when they are finished," Agamemnon said. "And we shall take home plunder rich enough to dazzle all the eyes in Greece. You have done well, brilliant Ulysses, with your idea of the Horse. You have won the war for us at last."

"Aye," said great-hearted Ulysses. "But will the god who put the idea in my head be pleased with what will happen in Troy tonight?"

Agamemnon stroked his short beard and watched a company of spearmen, led by swift-footed Diomedes, trot through the gate and fan out, brandishing their evil-looking spears and shouting.

"They want blood," said King Agamemnon. "Can you blame them? Ten years is a long time to be shivering in tents outside these walls, listening to the Trojans jeering at them from their safe towers. Ten bitter years, Ulysses. . . . Tell me, are *you* not longing to see your green island of Ithaca again, and your wife Penelope?"

"I am," replied Ulysses shortly. "But I am not longing to anger the gods. Will they smile on us if we behave like savages and turn helpless Troy into a pit of slaughter now?"

King Agamemnon shrugged his shoulders. "Ten bitter years . . ." he repeated.

Ulysses looked at him for a moment, then turned

away. "Come, lad," he said to Elpenor. "Let us see if we can find Priam! Come!"

Just inside the entrance to the splendid throne room of the royal palace, King Priam of Troy lay dead, his white hair matted with blood.

"Neoptolemus did this," Elpenor whispered to the scowling Ulysses. "Look!" he said, clutching his king by the arm and pointing. "He takes the Princess Cassandra away now."

At the far end of the dark hall, in a pool of moonlight under a window, Greek soldiers led away the white-robed Cassandra, sobbing, into slavery. The tall figure of Neoptolemus followed them out the doorway.

Ulysses gazed down at the blood-spattered corpse of Priam. Elpenor spoke:

"When his father was killed in battle, Neoptolemus swore that every man of Troy's royal house should die in return. Now only the child Astyanax is left."

Ulysses shook his helmeted head. "Shameful!" he muttered. "Senseless! Elpenor, we——

"*Look out!*" Ulysses cried suddenly. He shoved young Elpenor away with violence and fell quickly backward himself at the same time.

The spear passed between them, flashing in the moonlight, to clang against the wall.

Another spear instantly followed, to add its clatter and echo to the first, but now the two Greeks crouched in the shadows, their swords ready.

"Trojans," whispered Elpenor, searching the darkness.

"Aye," Ulysses answered softly. "We have work to do."

There was no sound in the dark room. For a long minute the keen-eyed Ulysses watched the flitting shadows along the opposite wall.

"Three," he whispered finally. "Or perhaps four."

As the four Trojan soldiers crept forward in the darkness, preparing to rush the outnumbered Greeks, a ringing clatter suddenly swung their attention to the door. It took them only an instant to discover that it was Ulysses' bronze helmet, bouncing and rolling along the marble floor where he had thrown it—but in that instant Ulysses and Elpenor were upon them from both sides with deadly fury. Ulysses, man of many wiles, had outwitted the Trojans once again.

With a two-handed swing of his heavy sword, the king of Ithaca severed a Trojan head. Then he dropped to one knee, blocking a smashing sword cut with his buckler, and brought his blade swiftly up under the shield of a second warrior. With a gurgling scream the Trojan fell. Ulysses rose and went to the aid of young Elpenor, who stood parrying the wild sword slashes of a third warrior. On the floor behind Elpenor still another soldier of Troy lay motionless in a black splash of his own blood. With a leap, Ulysses joined Elpenor, and together they cut down the last of the ill-fated Trojan attackers.

Panting from their headlong run up the stone steps, Ulysses and Elpenor gained the crest of the wall. They were too late.

Some distance away along the parapet, the wild-eyed Neoptolemus had just snatched the infant Astyanax, King Priam's grandchild, high up out of reach of its screaming mother. As they watched in horror, the young warrior hurled the wailing infant far out from the steep walls of Troy to its death on the rocky plain below.

Elpenor broke the silence first.

"Lord Neoptolemus has kept his vow," he said. "No male of Priam's family is left alive now."

Ulysses shook his head gravely and looked out to the west, to the sea that was just beginning to sparkle in the rosy-fingered dawn. Behind him he could hear the terrible screams of Trojans dying in the blood-slippery streets of their doomed city.

"Rich Troy is ours," he said, "but I am not proud of what is happening now."

"Nor I," said Elpenor, shuddering. "I wonder what the gods will think of it."

Ulysses did not answer, but still gazed out toward the west, toward Ithaca, with a troubled heart. He was thinking of the long journey home.

The Anger of the Gods

The return voyage began well. With the golden sun of morning beaming down upon them, the twelve crews under Ulysses' command launched their black ships and pointed them toward home. Ulysses himself supervised the last-minute preparations, striding from vessel to vessel along the yellow sand. He splashed through the foam at the sea's edge to inspect cargo lashings. The red-prowed ships were piled high with gold and silver, with tapestries and sparkling gems—booty from rich Troy. He ran his sunburned hand over oarlocks and water jars and neat coils of rope, and at last he nodded in satisfaction. All was ready.

Ulysses, the king of the Ithacans, gathered his veteran fighters about him for a final prayer and offering to glorious Zeus, the father of gods and men. The sun blazed down out of a clear sky; Ulysses lifted a golden cup in both hands and poured an offering of dark wine upon the sea. Then they leaped into the ships and pushed off.

Now Ulysses stood leaning against the deck rail at the high stern of the lead ship. He steadied himself against the roll of the sea and looked down. Below him fifty rowers pulled evenly and smoothly at their polished oars. There were smiles on the faces of his crewmen. The Ithacans were going home, after ten years. They were going home as victors, their black ships loaded with so much plunder and treasure that they rode low in the sparkling water.

There was no treasure left in Troy now, and not much of anything else, either. Ulysses squinted back at the Trojan plain, shading his eyes with his hand. He could see the square shape of the Scaean Gate tower outlined darkly against the green hills beyond the city. Winding down toward the yellow beach from Troy was a ragged line of captives, doomed to live as slaves in Greece, far across the sea.

Ulysses looked long and hard toward the shore, but he could no longer make out the erect figure of King Agamemnon standing where he had said his farewell to the Ithacans. All along the beach of gleaming sand, cutting the white foam line at the sea's edge, there were dark clusters of ships. The hundred vessels that had come with Agamemnon were there, together with the fifty ships of Neoptolemus, and many others. After ten years together the Greek kings, proud with victory, were separating for the return home.

Ulysses looked at the jagged shape of Troy at the head of its windy plain. From the dark ruins a few thin plumes of smoke were still streaming out across the bright sky.

"Troy's tale is finished," a voice said. It was the herald Eurybates. He held up his gleaming lyre and plucked one string. A clear note sounded, and then was snatched away by the breeze.

"Shall I sing of other things now, and shall we forget sad Troy?" he asked his king.

"Aye," said Ulysses, "sad Troy indeed." He sighed. "May the gods have more mercy on us than we had on the poor Trojans."

Then he threw an arm about the hunched shoulders of his old servant. "Well, sing me a cheerful song," the King of Ithaca said. He smiled and pointed out to the west, where a deep-bellied vessel with a wide sail of patched yellow rolled heavily in the water. "But first let us hoist sail and leave that lumbering wine boat behind."

"Hoist sail!" went the cry along the rowing benches. Up came the long oars, dripping cascades of sparkling drops that blew over the rowers' faces in a fine spray, as when a dog climbs out of a cool stream after a swim and shakes himself happily in the sun. The crewmen scrambled about, happy to be putting up the sail, happy to be sailing home to Ithaca at last.

They sang as they heaved the great mast of fir wood erect and set it in its socket in the cross-plank.

> *"Poseidon, O god of the terrible sea,*
> *O Earth-Shaker,*
> *Send us a fair wind for home, for home . . ."*

Eurybates plucked his silver lyre to keep the tune. They chanted as they hauled the stiff sail aloft with ropes of twisted hide. They sang a happy song as the wind came to swell out the white sail, so that the ship—all twelve ships—flew over the sun-glittering sea. The foam hissed against the painted bows.

> *"O Poseidon, O lord of the waves,*
> *We are in thy hands . . ."*

Behind them the white wakes gleamed brightly on the blue water. Above them was the friendly sun, and ahead of them was home.

After they had been at sea almost a week, Ulysses noticed a small black cloud off to the north behind them. The sea was still easy, friendly, dotted with bits of foam shining on the water of deep blue. The breeze held steady from the northeast; the sky was bright. But the little cloud followed them all morning.

By noon it had gained in size. Now it seemed as big as the sun. Still, the day was fair and the twelve vessels were making good headway over the vast sea. But the crews watched the cloud uneasily. What god had sent it, and what did it mean?

"It means trouble," said Eurylochus, one of Ulysses' soldier-captains. He tapped young Elpenor's arm and pointed. "Look how it moves up toward the sun."

Elpenor watched his king. Ulysses stood on the stern deck, near the helmsman at the steering oar. The sun glinted on his red hair and beard as he turned his head slowly to the west.

Eurylochus and Elpenor followed his gaze. A low spit of land was gradually coming into view on the horizon, dark between the bright sea and sky.

"Cape Malea," grunted Eurylochus. "The southern tip of Greece. We should reach it by evening, if the wind holds."

"And then will we sail around it, and north to Ithaca?" asked Elpenor.

"We will," answered Eurylochus. "*If* the wind holds."

Elpenor, his eyes still on the land, grinned and said, "It will be good to see——" He stopped suddenly as Eurylochus shot out a fierce hand and gripped his tunic. The swarthy soldier pulled the lad almost off the bench.

"Our wind!" he said hoarsely. "It's gone!"

It was true. The great sail had collapsed; it hung limp and still against the mast. The vessel was quickly losing speed, and had begun to wallow

The Greeks watched the great cloud uneasily

slightly. Now not a sound could be heard but the creaking of the ship's timbers and the slap of gray water against the hull.

For the sea, too, was suddenly different. The sparkle was gone. The brisk waves of blue, capped with white foam, had fallen into a gray swell that rolled heavily.

But Ulysses was not watching the sea: he was gazing upward toward the heavens. And in every one of the twelve ships the rest of the men were staring in the same direction.

The black cloud was swiftly covering the sun. The whole sky was growing dark as the cloud spread and built.

"What is it?" whispered Elpenor.

Eurylochus shook his head. "I don't know." He scowled. "Never have I seen such a thing. Behold, there is no other cloud anywhere, and this one moves without a wind." He shifted nervously on the bench.

"Take to the oars!" came a sharp command from Ulysses. "Lower sail! Row for land!" He stepped to the edge of the stern deck, above the rowing benches. Beside him Eurybates the herald, gripping the rail with one hand and his lyre with the other, shouted the king's order across the strangely quiet sea. In all the twelve ships under Ulysses' command, crewmen scrambled toward the masts and the limp sails.

They were too late. Suddenly the sky seemed to explode in a crackling thunderclap, filling the men's eardrums with sharp pain. The daylight vanished. Rolling down on them from the north came the black cloud, huge now, covering the sky, sputtering with forked lightning.

Then the wind struck with a rush. The first blast flattened the tiny boats against the sea and drove the breath from the crewmen's lungs. For an instant the world hung motionless, as though in the grip of some god's fierce hand.

Then suddenly wind and slashing rain, black sea and spitting lightning were everywhere. The sail of Ulysses' ship was torn to shreds as the wind buffeted the heavy mast in its box and bent it far over. A gray-black wave towered high above the stern, churning higher, higher . . . and then it came smashing down, breaking the deck rail to splinters.

Ulysses, salt water pouring over his head, was swept across the stern deck and down upon the rowing benches. He caught a glimpse of Eurybates, still clutching his silver lyre, tumbling past him in the black water. He saw the red bow of one of the other ships flash by and disappear.

Groping, the king felt a bench under his hands. He heaved himself up out of the water just as a dazzling bolt of lightning split the black sky. He saw a greenish-white ball of fire dance upon the tip of the mast, and then a solid sheet of water slashed across his face and engulfed him again.

But broad-shouldered Ulysses curled a strong arm

about the gunwale and pulled himself to his feet once more. Slowly, painfully, almost blinded by the driving rain, he hauled himself along, bit by bit in the teeth of the frenzied wind. Ahead of him on the empty stern deck he could catch glimpses of the long-shafted steering oar swinging crazily to and fro in the gale.

And then, as jagged lightning flashed, he saw Eurylochus and others of his valiant crew. They were also crawling along over the benches, doggedly working their way back toward the stern to reach the steering oar.

The vessel plunged and shuddered as the sea pounded her. The wild wind howled like the voice of some furious god.

"Where are we, sire?" Eurybates shouted the question into Ulysses' ear, cupping his two hands about his mouth to make himself heard over the roar of the wind. "Do you know?" the herald shouted.

Ulysses shook his head. He rubbed his salt-encrusted red beard and licked the brine from his lips. "Never have I been blown this far south," he shouted in answer. His salt-begrimed hair streamed over his face, and he brushed it back with one hand, but he did not loosen his hold on the great steering oar. The sea ran high still, and no sun's rays sparkled on the gray water. He looked up at the sky. Gone was the black storm cloud, but gone also was the bright sun.

Now the heavens were dull, soot gray, as though darkened by the smoke from a hundred burning cities.

Ulysses looked at his other long ships cutting through the waves with the spray blowing from their red-painted bows. No vessel had been lost in the hurricane, but six men out of every crew had been washed overboard.

The grim thought went across Ulysses' mind that Poseidon the sea god, the Earth-Shaker, must truly be angry. Seventy-two brave fighting men had been lost in the nine days and nights the wind had been raging. The Ithacans had been driven farther south now than any men had ever gone, deep into a strange world, a sunless world of gray. And still the wind blew.

On the morning of the tenth day they sighted land ahead of them to the south. Then the wind stopped, suddenly.

The twelve black ships clustered together, rocking this way and that on the turbulent sea. The crews made solemn offerings to the gods for their drowned comrades. Then they unshipped the long oars and fitted them to the leather-covered oarlocks.

By noon, when the sun would have been shining high above them—if there had been a sun—they ran the red prows of their ships up on the unknown beach.

As the seamen hauled the heavy anchor stones wearily over the sides, a flock of green-and-yellow birds came swooping and screeching along the shore. Ulysses watched the birds fly back into the jungle-like forest that came down to the edge of the beach. "After we have eaten and drunk," he said to tall Eurylochus, "take two men and see what lies beyond those trees."

Eurylochus nodded, and flexed his long legs to accustom them to the land. "I'll go now, sire," he said. "Then we can sooner be on our way home again."

Ulysses smiled. "Take two reliable men," he said, clapping his brave captain on the shoulder. Eurylochus strode off briskly. He fingered the bronze sword at his side as he went.

The gray sky had shadowed into dusk when the three men returned, walking slowly out of the jungle toward the beached ships.

Eurylochus, in the lead, was smiling dreamily; a cluster of red-and-pink flowers hung at his belt, over the worn hilt of his bronze sword. The two strong fighting-men he had taken with him wore garlands of the red-and-pink flowers on their heads and around their shoulders. They jostled each other as they walked, like contented puppies after a meal.

The crews left their campfires and ran forward to crowd around the three tall men.

"What did you find, Eurylochus?"

The big captain grinned. "Why are you all standing here?" he asked. "Don't you want to eat?"

He lifted his hand before their eyes. It held one of the large red-and-pink flowers. "It's good," he said, nibbling a petal slowly. "I don't remember eating anything better."

He sat down on the sand and stretched his legs out in front of him. Then he picked up a handful of sand and idly watched it trickle through his fingers. "This is a nice evening, isn't it?" he asked. He chuckled contentedly.

"Eurylochus!" said Ulysses. "What has happened to you?" He bent down and shook the big man's shoulder. "We sail home—have you forgotten?—to Ithaca!"

The bronzed captain, brave in war, looked up at his king strangely.

"Ithaca?" he asked. "Where is that?"

"Ithaca is your home!" said Ulysses.

"No," said Eurylochus. "This is my home, right here. I have been here all my life."

He plucked a large petal and tasted it delicately. He held the rest of the blossom up to the scowling Ulysses. "Lotus flower," he said, smiling. "Eat it. It will make you feel wonderful. It will take away all your cares."

Ulysses took the soft flower from him and examined it curiously, turning it over in a scarred and salt-grimed hand. "Aye, it will take away my cares," said Ulysses, "and my memory too."

He looked at the three powerful warriors. They

The three strong fighting-men were wearing flowers

smiled lazily back at him and nibbled the lotus blossoms.

Behind the flower-garlanded soldiers, tall trees swayed gently in the dusk, like beckoning arms. From the beach where the black ships lay there came the sound of the cold sea pounding harshly on the shore. But from the land, a warm breeze wafted the sweet scent of the lotus flowers over the ships, over Ulysses and his crewmen, weary of battles and of the terrible sea.

"Up!" snapped Ulysses.

The brawny hand of the Ithacan king suddenly descended upon Eurylochus and yanked him violently to his feet. Bewildered, the captain blinked his eyes and smiled foolishly.

"Elpenor," commanded Ulysses, "take him back to the ship."

"No!" cried Eurylochus. "No, I belong here!" Two large tears began to trickle down the warrior's tanned cheeks. He turned to run back toward the trees, clutching the lotus blossoms.

But Ulysses tightened his grip and hauled his weeping captain forward. "Tie him up!" he ordered sternly. "Bind all three of them, put them aboard the ships!"

There was a pause. Several of the crewmen started forward, then stopped. They stared in fascination at the bright, tempting lotus, and they hesitated.

"*Do as I say!*" bellowed Ulysses the king, his red beard bristling. "Take them down to the ships. We sail away at once! *Obey me!*"

The crew obeyed. Eurylochus and his two companions were put, wailing and struggling, aboard the red-prowed ships, and the campfires along the beach were stamped out. As grunting crewmen heaved the great anchor stones up and into the vessels, Eurybates approached his king on the darkening beach.

"Sire," he said, "putting to sea at night can be dangerous." He frowned at the jagged line of surf breaking upon the shore.

"I think this flower of forgetfulness is more dangerous still," said Ulysses softly. With the toe of his sandal he touched a red-and-pink blossom lying at their feet. They both looked down at the flower for a moment. Then Ulysses ground the delicate blossom into the sand beneath his heel and hurried toward the ships.

The Cave of Death

"Ride the surf in!" shouted Ulysses to the commander of the next ship. He clung to the rail as his own vessel rolled in the heavy swell. "Make for that cove at the foot of the cliff!" He pointed to where evil-looking waves smashed upon the rocks of the bleak island. Dawn had just come—the ninth dawn, gray and dull, since they had left the tempting land of the lotus flowers.

Ulysses turned to the rowing benches. "Back water as you go!" he shouted, trying to make himself heard above the surf's thundering.

Young Elpenor cupped his hands about his mouth and leaned close to his king's ear. "Someone lives here," he said, pointing to a column of smoke that rose into the gray sky from beyond the cliff top. Elpenor grinned. "Where there is a fire perhaps there is warm food for us!" He rubbed his hands together.

Ulysses laughed and pushed the youthful soldier firmly toward the rowing benches. "First let us get to the island," he said. "Then we can see about filling our stomachs."

King Ulysses' ship was the first one in. Spray flying about its red bow, it came riding over a great breaker's foaming crest and landed with a mighty splash upon the calm water of the cove. The rowers leaned forward powerfully on their oars, backing water as the vessel glided up to the beach, close under a steep cliff.

When they had anchored, they turned to watch the other fast-running vessels come in. One by one the curved prows came into sight amidst the foam, and the slim black ships danced across the breakers into the cove.

When all twelve vessels were safely beached, Ulysses vaulted the gunwale and splashed ashore. He summoned his captains to him. They left the ships and clustered around their king on the narrow beach dotted with sea wrack and broken shells. Ulysses pointed to an inlet at the cove's far end. "I think that will be a better way out when we leave," he said. "Through that passage."

The Ithacan king stared up from under reddish eyebrows, caked with salt, toward the top of the cliff. "And there"—he indicated a narrow path winding up the cliff face—"there is a way we can go up," he said.

"We will see what manner of men live here. I'll take twelve men with me. Polites, you choose them—yourself and eleven others."

A stout captain, bald and round-faced, flashed a wide smile at his king and trotted off toward the ships.

"With full armor!" Ulysses called after him. And he stood there, gazing up at the grim cliff, while Eurybates brought armor and keen-edged sword and silently helped his king buckle them on.

The climb was slow and difficult. The thirteen men, Ulysses in the lead, crept carefully up along the cliff face, clinging to roots and bushes and projecting rocks. Their heavy armor weighed them down, and the plumes of their burnished helmets caught on brambles, but up they climbed. Often the narrow path became only a vague scratch on the rock, and once or twice it disappeared completely, but they climbed steadily upward, wedging their toes in crevices when there was no branch or shrub to grasp.

At long last Ulysses cautiously raised his helmeted head above the cliff top. Facing him, a short distance away, was the gaping black mouth of an enormous cave, as high as half a dozen tall men.

Polites, breathing hard, hauled himself up beside his king. The two men looked at the cave in silence. Nothing moved but the horsehair plumes atop their helmets, ruffling gently in the wind.

"It seems to be the home of a shepherd," Ulysses

said finally. He pointed to a sheepfold of piled stones on the grassy slope outside the cave. Then, lifting a knee over the cliff edge, he heaved himself forward and stood erect on the grass.

"Bring the men up," he said to Polites. "I do not think this shepherd will mind if we rest in his cave until he returns."

The Greeks were waiting in the half-light at the back of the cave when its owner finally came home. They heard feet crashing through the underbrush outside, and then the bleating of sheep.

"I hope the shepherd is friendly," murmured Elpenor. "I've eaten a lot of his cheese."

"Don't worry, there is enough here for many men," said Polites, waving his hand at the cave wall, where long shelves held piles of cheeses and jugs of milk. "Elpenor, where is that wineskin we brought?"

asked Ulysses. "We will make him a present of it to show our good will."

Now the entrance was darkened by a shadow, and the shepherd came into his cave.

"Zeus on Olympus!" hissed Polites.

It was a giant. His legs were like tree trunks. He had to stoop and bend his head to pass through the entrance that was as high as six tall men. Once inside, he straightened up and threw an enormous load of firewood to the floor with a great crash. Billows of choking dust rose toward the ceiling. Then he squatted on his vast haunches and lit a fire.

He leaned his shaggy head down to blow on the kindling out of a mouth the size of a great black cooking cauldron. The teeth he bared were like yellow ax blades. Then the sparks caught, and a lick of orange flame danced up, lighting his face.

He had only one eye. It was in the center of his forehead.

When he had driven all his bleating sheep inside, he rolled and shoved a tremendous boulder across the cave mouth, sealing it like a corked bottle. Then he took a tree trunk as big as a ship's mast and stirred up the fire.

When the light glinted and flashed on the bronze armor of the Greek warriors, he swung his head around toward the back of the cave and blinked his huge yellowish eye.

"Who are you?" he roared, letting the tree trunk fall with a crash. He thrust his massive head down at the little band of Greeks. "Where do you come from?" he bellowed, and the walls of the cave seemed to vibrate.

Ulysses squared his shoulders and stepped forward. "We are Greeks," he said. His words rang out over the rumbling echoes of the giant's voice.

"Greeks? What do you want here?"

"We were sailing home from Troy, good sir, when the gods sent winds that blew us off our course." Ulysses spread his hands out, palms upward, and smiled a broad smile. "We are here in friendship," he said. "Will you not show us hospitality such as the gods decree for strangers in distress?"

He waited, hands outstretched, smiling up at the giant in the wavering firelight. There was no sound in the vast cave but the crackling of the fire and the heavy rasping of the giant's breath.

Then the giant straightened up. He roared with wild laughter, throwing back his head so that it was almost lost to sight in the gloom of the high-vaulted cave. The thundering peals of his laughter echoed in the darkness.

"Fool!" he roared. "What care I about a god's decree? You know nothing of this country, fool," he thundered. "You do not know that a Cyclops is stronger than any god of yours! Little fool!" And his wild shouts of laughter rebounded from the dim walls, shaking the hearts of the tiny Greeks.

The giant leaned down again suddenly, choking off a laugh. "Tell me," he said, more quietly now, "where did you leave your ship? Is she anchored close by?" His single eye gleamed blearily and his look darted from side to side. The cave was deathly silent now, for the giant was holding his breath.

"Alas," said the crafty Ulysses after a moment, "we have no ship any more. Poseidon wrecked it as we tried to land, and"—he gestured toward his crewmen —"we are the only survivors."

The giant Cyclops blew out his breath in a great snort, and then he spoke no more. But his two long arms, thick and hairy, came reaching forward suddenly out of the darkness. Nails that were like blackened claws glistened in the firelight. The hands clutched two Greek soldiers, armor and all, and snatched them up into the air, screaming in terror.

Their screams were cut off abruptly as the giant, lifting the men high over his head into the blackness of the upper cave, hurled them at the rocky wall. Their armor clanged loudly, and as the metallic echoes died away their bodies lay broken in the dust, motionless, lifeless.

And strangely, in the midst of all his horror at this sight, a thought struck Ulysses:

So must the child Astyanax have died, when he was flung from the walls of Troy.

The horror did not end there. For the Cyclops then picked up the dead men and ate them. He washed the meal down with a sloshing bucket of milk, yawned, sucked his teeth contentedly, and then stretched out among his sheep.

As his rumbling snores blew dust from the walls about them, the Greeks huddled together, sick with fear. The fire slowly died, and the darkness was complete.

Elpenor was the first to break the terrified silence. "Let us all draw swords and kill the monster in his sleep," he said hoarsely, his voice trembling.

There came a short, bitter laugh, and then Polites' deep voice. "We could do that, yes. But what then?"

"Aye," said Ulysses calmly in the darkness. "We would die anyway. Who but the Cyclops can roll away that stone?"

More silence, broken only by the thunderous snores of the giant and an occasional bleat from a sheep. Finally Polites grunted and said, "Well, he cannot kill us while he sleeps. We might as well sleep ourselves." And his armor scraped as he settled himself.

"Yes," said Ulysses thoughtfully. "Sleep, men. We will talk in the morning."

Some of the Greeks murmured together for a long time, but most of them finally slept. Ulysses himself sat awake all night, staring into the cold blackness of the cave and thinking, thinking.

By morning he had a plan. The Cyclops said not a word to them when he awoke, but the great hands came groping in the darkness and clutched two more men. When the monster had crunched and swallowed them, he rolled the huge boulder from the cave mouth and drove his sheep out to graze.

The Greeks, crouching at the back of the cave,

caught a glimpse of morning in the world outside. A cool sea breeze blew into the cave, and a bird flew by. They could hear the surf pounding on the shore where their comrades waited. Then the giant rolled back the stone and was gone, and they were in darkness again.

Now Ulysses got to his feet. He felt about in the dark until he found the massive olive-wood pole, as large as the mast of a twenty-oared ship, which the monster had used to stir the fire. He called Polites to him. They drew their sharp swords and together hacked off a piece longer than a man.

By the time the Cyclops could be heard returning, one end of the heavy pole had been whittled and sharpened down to a point. It lay hidden behind a pile of stones at the back of the cave.

The boulder was rolled from the doorway, and the first of the sheep ambled into the cave. The crewmen could see that night was beginning to fall outside. They could also see the outlines of the giant's two legs, like vast trees in the dusk. The Cyclops bent his shaggy head to the cave mouth and peered in at them, blinking his single eye.

"He's choosing his dinner," whispered Polites. He nudged Elpenor. "Hide yourself, lad. You look young and tender." He slapped his own generous stomach and gave a wry laugh. "But 'tis true there's more meat on *my* bones, eh?" He watched the outside world disappear as the last of the sheep came in and the stone was rolled across the entrance again.

When the Cyclops had built a fire, he killed and ate two more of Ulysses' crew, valiant swordsmen, farmers from the Greek mainland near Ithaca. He sent a great bucket of milk gurgling down his throat after them and wiped his mouth with the back of a hairy paw. Sitting against the cave wall, he stretched his enormous legs out toward the fire. His great eye gleamed with a yellow light as he sucked his teeth.

Ulysses nodded to Elpenor. The youth raised the bulging wineskin he had carried with him from the ship, and poured full a huge wooden bowl they had found among the milk pails. Ulysses took it and stepped forward.

"Here, Cyclops," he said loudly, his voice ringing in the lofty cave, "here is a sample of the wine we carried in our ship. I meant to make you a present of it, but you have not been a very good host to us."

He held the brimming bowl of wine high in his two arms, so that the rich vapors floated up to the giant's nostrils.

The monster bent his head and fixed his eye on the Ithacan king. Then he snorted, and seized the wooden bowl. He tipped it up into the great cavern that was his mouth, gulping greedily, stopping for a moment to smack his lips, then swilling the strong wine down again.

When the deep bowl was empty he stretched it out toward Ulysses.

"More!" he gasped, his eye glittering. His voice shook the racks of milking pails on the cave walls.

As Ulysses took the huge bowl to be filled once again, the monster thundered, "And tell me your name, that I may reward you."

But the wily king of the Ithacans said nothing. He held the bowl aloft a second time, and the Cyclops grabbed at it eagerly and drank. The dark wine ran down his chin from the corners of his mouth and dripped on the cave floor. It splashed on Ulysses as he stood waiting in silence, watching the monster drink.

"More!" roared the Cyclops, holding out the bowl.

Ulysses filled it a third time with the powerful wine, and the Cyclops finished it off in a single draught. Then he flung the bowl from him, to clatter against the far wall of the cave.

The monster leaned back, puffing, and turned his single eye to Ulysses again. "What is your name?" he wheezed.

"I am called Noman, good sir," said Ulysses. "I am glad you liked my wine," he added.

"Good wine," grunted the Cyclops. "For such good wine I will reward you, Noman." He leaned forward suddenly and pointed a great dirty finger at the Greek king.

"As a reward," he rumbled, "I shall eat Noman last of all!" And he fell back against the cave wall, shaking with mighty laughter, roaring and sputtering until the tears came to his eye. Still laughing at his joke, he rolled over on the floor of the cave among his sheep. Still laughing, muttering drunkenly, he fell

The five men staggered forward under their load

at last into a deep sleep.

Ulysses motioned to his waiting men. They dragged the great pole from its hiding place and hauled it forward to the fire. They shoved the pointed end into the heart of the crackling blaze, turning it over and over until the tip smoked, and then glowed red-hot. Stretched on his back beside them, the giant snored away.

" 'Tis ready!" whispered Ulysses. Then he and four of his strong crewmen laid hold of the tree trunk and, with a mighty heave, lifted it to their shoulders. The sharpened point glowed red in the darkness, lighting up the crewmen's intent faces.

The five men staggered forward under their load, up to where the firelight glinted on the craggy face of the monster. The Cyclops grunted suddenly and rolled over to face them. They waited, holding their breaths.

But his eye stayed closed. He snored deeply, and then blew out a rasping breath that sent a shower of stinging sparks flying over the Greeks from the end of the glowing pole.

"Higher!" whispered Ulysses. The sleeping giant began to stir again.

"Now!"

They lurched up to the monster and plunged the red-hot timber into his eye.

There was a crackling hiss, and a cloud of steam poured forth. The monster bellowed and screamed. Blood boiled in his vast eye socket, and flying drops spattered the Greeks as they dropped the tree trunk and leaped away.

An acrid smell of burning flesh filled the cave. Ulysses and his men watched as the blind Cyclops thrashed wildly, screaming, sobbing, clutching at his face, pounding the earth. They watched and waited. The awakened sheep milled about, bleating in fear.

Soon noises were heard outside the mouth of the cave. Thunderous footsteps jarred the ground; rumbling voices sounded.

"More giants!" Elpenor whispered.

Now a great shout came from outside. "Polyphemus! What is it? Why do you scream? Is someone killing you?"

Elpenor gripped the arm of Polites. "What will happen to us now?" he asked.

"Wait and see, lad," Polites answered. "Your king expected this."

They looked at Ulysses in the firelight. He was smiling grimly.

Another shout came from the giants outside the cave. "Is someone trying to kill you?"

The monster struggled to his knees and clutched the boulder in the entranceway.

"Noman is killing me!" he roared. "Noman!"

The echoes of his shout died away in the lofty cave, and then the answering shout came from outside.

"No man is killing you? Then go back to sleep, Polyphemus! If no man is bothering you, go back to your dreams!" And the voices went away, and so did the ground-shaking footsteps. The Cyclops kneeled against the stone in the light of the dying fire, gasping and sobbing and moaning.

He stayed there until dawn. The Greeks meanwhile were quietly busy, under the whispered orders of their king. They took the giant's sheep and bound them together in threes, side by side. And under the middle sheep of each three the wily Ulysses tied one of his crewmen. Hidden thus under the bellies of the sheep, they waited for morning. Ulysses sat by the largest of the flock, a huge black-fleeced ram, and watched the blinded Cyclops.

Finally it was dawn outside, and the monster stirred himself. Grunting and sobbing, he rolled the great entrance stone aside. Then he sat by the edge of the cave mouth and called to his sheep.

The flock began to move forward, anxious to nibble the sweet grass outside. As the bleating sheep passed, bearing the crewmen underneath, the giant felt their backs with his huge hands, running his fingers over their curly wool to make sure no Greeks were astride them.

When the last of his men was safely outside, Ulysses seized the fleece of the great black ram and swung himself under its belly. He clung there, facing upward, and let the animal carry him out of the cave, past the searching fingers of the terrible Cyclops, out to the world at last.

He quickly untied his crewmen, and they all clam-

He snatched up a boulder as big as the top of a mountain

bered down the steep cliff to where their anxious comrades waited. Then they leaped aboard the long ships and rowed silently out of the inlet and toward the open sea.

But the proud Ulysses could not leave the island without a final word to their enemy. Standing at the rail of his vessel as it cleared the inlet, he faced the top of the cliff and raised a great shout.

"Polyphemus! O Cyclops!"

There was a mighty answering bellow, and the giant appeared at the edge of the cliff.

"Cyclops," called Ulysses, "when people ask who blinded you, tell them it was Ulysses, son of Laertes and king of Ithaca!"

Polyphemus gave a roar of rage and stretched his long arms out toward the sea.

"O Poseidon!" he shouted. "O my father, O Earth-Shaker, take vengeance on this vile Greek who has blinded your son!"

And he snatched up a boulder as big as the top of a mountain and hurled it blindly out to sea, toward the taunting voice of Ulysses.

It fell beyond the ships, with a splash that darkened the sky. The wave it made almost carried them back to shore. But they rowed strongly and at last began to pull away from the island. As they rowed they looked back toward the Cyclops, high on his cliff top. He stood outlined against the heavens like the topmost crag of some great volcano.

"Whom the Gods Hate . . ."

The wind blew, pungent with sea salt. It blew about the head of old King Aeolus, and streamed out his long gray beard. He stood on the beach of his island, surrounded by Ulysses and the other Greeks.

"Marvelous!" King Aeolus cried happily, clapping Ulysses on the shoulder. "Marvelous! Great horses of wood, and one-eyed giants—I shall never forget your wonderful stories, never!" He chuckled and shook his head in delight. "Not since Zeus first made me Keeper of the Winds have I enjoyed myself so much."

Ulysses grinned back at him. "And not since we set sail from Troy have we known such kind hospitality, King Aeolus." He waved a tanned arm toward his companions. "When we landed here we were tired, sore at heart, half starving. . . . Look at us now." He smiled at Elpenor standing with the sea breeze ruffling his fresh white tunic. "After all these days of feasting my young friend here looks more like a well-fed cat than a sailor. And so do they all, every one of my crewmen. You have been good to us, and if my stories have pleased you that is small payment."

"Aye!" the crewmen chorused. "Long live King Aeolus!" And then they went hurrying down to the seaside, to the twelve black ships lined up at the water's edge.

Left alone, Ulysses and the old king watched the crews bustling about the red-prowed ships. "Will you and your men not stay longer?" Aeolus asked. "You are still welcome."

"Thank you, sire, but we must be on our way. We have rested and feasted long enough." Ulysses almost had to shout to be heard above the gusty wind. He leaned close to the ear of the gray-bearded king. "But we are grateful to you."

"Well," Aeolus said, his eyes sparkling merrily, "I have one gift to give you still."

"Oh, no!" protested Ulysses politely.

"Yes! It will be an easy thing for me—Zeus has given me power over all the winds. Harken to me now, brave Greek." The wind seemed to die down while Aeolus spoke, so that Ulysses could hear him clearly. But it blew again when he had finished speaking.

It blew steadily and cleanly as they clambered aboard their ships and waved farewell to the friendly

old king. It blew more strongly still when they had hoisted the sails. And it blew in only one direction —toward Ithaca.

For that was the gift King Aeolus, Keeper of the Winds, had made to Ulysses. One steady wind to blow the Greeks safely home at last. A wind that blew for nine days and nights, sending the twelve ships skimming eagerly over the gray sea.

Ulysses sat at the stern of his vessel with the long tiller under his hand. At his feet lay a great leather bag that Aeolus had given him. It was sealed with a silver wire. Only Ulysses knew that it contained all the winds of the world except the friendly one that was blowing them home.

Nine days and nights the same wind blew, and Ulysses never left the tiller. With all the other winds trapped in the bag at his feet, nothing now could keep him and his men from home. And on the tenth day they saw their native land.

They recognized their beloved Ithaca at once, making it out on the horizon as the dawn began to light the dark sea. They could see shepherds' fires twinkling brightly in the fields, like tiny welcoming lamps.

Their voyage was nearly over at last. Ulysses heaved a deep sigh of happiness, yawned, and gave the tiller to Elpenor. Then he stretched out on a bench and slept.

It was his second mistake. His first had been not telling the crewmen what the bag contained. For the moment he fell asleep, the crew fell to whispering, all along the benches, about the mysterious leather bag. Some thought it held gold. All of them thought there would be no harm in undoing the silver wire. Just a quick look inside—that was all they wanted.

The vast roaring as the furious winds were loosed woke Ulysses, but too late, too late. For in a trice the little vessels were caught in the grip of a howling windstorm, with gales such as the world had never seen. And the fierce winds never stopped until they had blown home to their keeper again, driving the ships back to the island of King Aeolus.

This time the old king was not so happy to see the Greeks. He stood on the sandy shore and watched them approach. The winds had died down at last, suddenly. The sails hung limp in the strange silence as the ships were rowed slowly up to the beach.

Aeolus' sharp eyes flitted across the stern of the

first vessel as it glided toward him. He could see the leather bag, lying collapsed and empty on the deck, its silver wire twisted upon it uselessly.

Grim-faced, King Aeolus waited until the red prow of Ulysses' ship grated on the sand before him. Then he said, his voice ringing harshly in the windless air, "Whom the gods hate I will not help!"

He turned his back on them and walked away. Not a breath of air stirred anywhere. The gray sea was motionless, without a ripple. Slowly the Greeks turned their black ships toward Ithaca and began to row again.

The Sorceress

"I believe King Aeolus was right. The gods do hate us," said Elpenor to his king on a cold afternoon a week later. He shook his head sadly and stared at the empty sea. There were tears in his eyes. "Yesterday we had twelve ships——"

"And today we have one," finished Ulysses. "Aye, Elpenor, the gods are cruel indeed." He put an arm about the young man's shoulders. There was a long silence. "Well," Ulysses said finally, with a sigh, "at least we can be thankful that we escaped and that a few of us are still alive." He looked along the rowing benches, where a handful of his brave crewmen sat, each with his own black thoughts, each with his unhappy memories of yesterday's terrible battle.

They had rowed away from the island of Aeolus, Keeper of the Winds, for six weary, windless days.

On the seventh day they came to a rocky island that none of them knew. There was a little harbor, ringed round with steep hills. No houses could be seen, but a plume of smoke rose peacefully from somewhere beyond the hills. Clustering together outside the harbor, the twelve ships rocked back and forth on the sea swell while Ulysses and his captains held conference. Then they noticed a maiden, young and slim, carrying a water jar along the shore. She waved to them cheerfully.

She had seemed so friendly, Ulysses thought now, shuddering. His own vessel had rowed over, and Elpenor had eagerly splashed ashore to talk to the girl. Meanwhile the other eleven ships moved slowly along the shoreline until they reached the harbor entrance. Then they turned out of sight into the narrow passage and rowed between the hills to the peaceful harbor.

They had been caught in a fearful trap. For no sooner had the crewmen moored the long ships, dropping the anchor stones into the shallow water along the inner beach, than a horde of screeching savages, as tall as giants, poured over the hilltops. They sent gigantic boulders thundering down the slopes, to crash into the slim, beautiful Greek boats and shatter them to splinters. And behind the boulders came the savages, howling down the hillsides, brandishing sharp spears.

The Greeks tried bravely to fight, but they had no chance. Their ships were smashed and capsized. Crewmen and captains were speared like fish as they floundered in the water, struggling to reach the shore. The placid water of the bay was churned into a horrible foam of blood and wreckage and corpses.

By the time Ulysses' vessel, following behind, had reached the harbor the slaughter was complete. Ulysses looked into the bay, and he could not believe what his eyes saw. Eleven proud and well-manned ships had entered here a short time before. Now he saw only a litter of black wreckage amid bloody foam. And the hillsides swarmed with shrieking savages.

Ulysses saw the jagged remains of one vessel's stern jutting up out of the blood-darkened water near him. The body of dark-haired Eurybates the herald, a spear through his chest, slid down the tilted deck and plunged into the water as Ulysses watched.

Suddenly a huge stone splashed near by, and new

yells were heard. The savages had seen them. Ulysses hesitated, looking into the bay. But there was nothing to be done. He swung the tiller about and, under a hail of spears, he and his men rowed for their lives.

Now, a day later, Ulysses sat brooding, his arm about young Elpenor's shoulders. He did not move as the youth spoke.

"Laestrygones," said Elpenor. "That is what the girl called the tribe." He shuddered violently. "I shall never forget the name."

"And I shall never forget my trusty Eurybates," said Ulysses, half to himself.

Elpenor looked up. "He must have fought bravely."

"I am sure they all did," Ulysses said. "But who can fight the will of the gods?"

"Why should the gods will us this misfortune?" asked Elpenor.

Ulysses frowned. "I know not," he said thoughtfully. And he sat gazing at the gray horizon. He looked toward the east, toward Troy and its pitiful ruins. Did the answer lie there?

That same day they came to another island. Finding a sheltered cove, they scouted about cautiously before beaching the ship. But this time no giant savages attacked them. All seemed peaceful; they disembarked.

For two days they rested, praying to the immortal

gods, mourning their dead comrades who had gone forever to the dark world below. On the third day Ulysses took his spear and his sharp sword and climbed to a hilltop. He saw a plume of smoke in the distance.

"Smoke!" cried Eurylochus when Ulysses announced what he had seen. "That was what greeted us on the island of the Laestrygones! And on the island of the Cyclops before that! Is it an evil omen again? Are we *all* to be killed this time?"

Some of the crewmen groaned aloud, and a few leaped to their feet and started for the ship.

"It may not be an evil omen," said Ulysses. "We shall see." And he ordered the crewmen to divide into two bands. He appointed Eurylochus leader of one, and he himself took command of the other. Then into a bronze helmet he put two pebbles, one for Eurylochus and one for himself.

The crewmen crowded around as the helmet was shaken. The pebbles rattled noisily against the bronze; then one stone flew out and fell on the sand. There was silence as the men bent over it.

"It is yours," said Ulysses quietly. He held out his hand to Eurylochus. "May the gods protect you."

The tall captain straightened up and took his king's hand. "Start now," Ulysses said. "We will wait one full day for you."

Eurylochus nodded grimly and strode off up the hill that sloped away from the little cove. Behind him went Polites and young Elpenor and twenty other well-armed men. As they gained the hilltop they stared nervously at the thin column of smoke that hung in the air far ahead of them.

In a short time Eurylochus was back—alone. He came clattering down the slope, brambles tearing at him, and when he reached the waiting men he was so flushed and excited he could hardly speak. But he finally blurted out his story.

"We went beyond the hill—through a heavy thicket—came to a clearing." He gasped for breath and looked back fearfully over his shoulder. "I—I alone escaped," he said.

"Escaped from what? Where are the others?"

Eurylochus took a deep breath and then spoke very quickly. "There is a small palace of marble—we heard a woman's voice singing, very sweetly—we went closer to look inside. Then great wolves and lions sprang upon us——"

"Did you fight them?"

"No, it was very strange. They were harmless, and played about us like puppies. While we were marveling at this, a beautiful woman with dark hair came to the threshold. She invited us in, offered us a feast."

The tall captain stopped for breath again, and shuddered.

"What happened then? Out with it!" said Ulysses.

The perspiration gleamed on Eurylochus' forehead as he looked at the anxious faces around him. "They all went in, but I feared a trap and hid outside. I watched through a window," he said. "I saw her give them food and drink, and then——" He took a long breath. "And then she turned them all into swine!"

"Into pigs?" asked someone unbelievingly.

Eurylochus nodded. "She has them shut up in a pigsty now." He sat down on a rock and put his head in his hands.

There was a long moment of silence. Then Ulysses spoke.

"A sorceress," he said. "I have heard of such." He lifted his heavy bronze helmet in both hands and set it on his head. "Wait here. I will see what there is to be done." And he set off up the slope.

He had gone perhaps half the distance, brooding darkly, his heart troubled, when he met a god.

The god looked much like an ordinary young man, but there was light glowing all around him on the dark forest path. When Ulysses saw this, and when he saw the pointed cap and the shining wand of gold, he knew that Hermes, messenger of the powerful gods, stood before him.

He waited, frightened, but the god said, "Have no fear. I am here to give you help. Foolish man, did you think to master the sorceress Circe all by yourself?"

The god laughed pleasantly at Ulysses, who stood bewildered and silent before him. Then the god held out his hand. In it was a plant, freshly pulled from the earth. The root was black as coal, and the blossom was milky white.

"Take it," said the messenger-god. "It will protect you."

Ulysses swallowed, and finally was able to speak. "What is it?" he asked.

"We call it *moly,*" the god answered. "It is an herb. Take it, Ulysses, and listen to me. Circe will welcome you and give you food and drink. They will be filled with strong drugs. But you can swallow everything without fear—the moly will protect you. Then, when the sorceress tries to change you into a groveling pig, draw your sharp sword and rush at her as if to kill her."

The god shook his head warningly. "Even when she is frightened," he said, "she may try to trick you. Never forget that she is a sorceress, and not like other humans. But when she sees that her drugs have failed, you should be able to bend her to your will."

The immortal Hermes smiled. "With my herb, and with your own stout heart, you are well armed, Ulysses." And he walked away into the dark wood.

For a long time Ulysses wondered if he had been dreaming. Had he really been visited by a god? It was hard to believe, as he stood alone in the dark and silent forest.

Still, there was the moly. He turned it over and over in his fingers while he walked on toward Circe's palace. Was it really the gift of a god?

Ulysses raised his sharp sword menacingly

Perhaps the herb helped, or perhaps it was Ulysses' own courage, but Circe did not weave a spell over him. She was very beautiful indeed, with her black hair reaching down her back to her waist, and with her glittering eyes—the eyes of a sorceress. They made his head swim, those burning eyes. But Ulysses thought of his waiting wife Penelope, and of Ithaca, green in the sunshine, and he raised his sharp sword menacingly.

The sorceress agreed to do his bidding. She lifted her strange enchantment from the crewmen, and finally all Ulysses' comrades were back with him again—all except one.

Between Scylla and Charybdis

"Where is Elpenor?" Ulysses asked the crew when they were at last ready to go back to the ship and set sail.

Polites laughed. "Eating grapes," he said, pointing to a corner of Circe's palace. A giant grapevine, green and black and purple against the white stone, climbed up the wall and over the flat roof.

Ulysses followed the vine up with his eyes. At the top he saw the broad back of Elpenor, outlined against the sky. The youth was sitting on the roof edge, his feet dangling among the grape leaves, and as Ulysses watched he threw his head back and lifted a huge bunch of purple grapes to his open mouth.

Laughing, Ulysses said, "He will never get home to Ithaca that way." And then he shouted, "Elpenor!"

What happened next was so sudden that Ulysses' shout still hung in the air when it was over. Young Elpenor, turning toward his king's voice, lost his balance and fell from the roof.

The vine leaves were still quivering when Ulysses reached the spot. He dropped to one knee over the sprawling body. The youth was dead.

After a long silence, during which the other crewmen crowded about, Ulysses finally looked up.

"I meant him no harm," he told Polites sadly.

"Poor lad," Polites said. "May his soul have a safe journey to the House of Hades."

Later, before sailing, they stood at the shore and prayed solemnly to the all-seeing gods for the spirit of their dead comrade. When they had finished they planted the youth's oar upright in the mound of fresh earth that marked his resting place.

Circe watched from the edge of the dark wood, her white robes gleaming in the shadow of the trees. The crewmen looked nervously back over their shoulders at her as they stood beside Elpenor's tomb. But the sorceress did nothing more to them.

She spoke only once before they clambered into their red-prowed ship and pushed off. "Ulysses," she said, coming closer and putting her white hand on the Ithacan king's brown wrist, "man of trouble, I will give you three warnings. If you are wise you will harken to them.

"First," she said, fixing her terrible eyes upon him,

"Untie me!" Ulysses shouted. But the rowers heard

"let not your crewmen listen to the sweet voices of the Sirens, or you will never see your Ithaca again. Second, when you must pass between the monster Scylla and the whirlpool Charybdis, remember that Charybdis is the more deadly. Three times a day she sucks down the sea, and three times a day she spews it forth again. Beware Charybdis, Ulysses! And third, harm not the cattle of the sun, no matter how great your pangs of hunger. If you touch the sacred cattle, ruin will come to your ship and your comrades."

She smiled her strange smile, and slipped away through the trees.

The adventure of the Sirens was like a dream. All

nothing, not the Sirens' song nor their king's shouting

sound stopped; the sighing wind fell quiet and the surging waves were still. An eerie silence blanketed the sea as the rowers pulled the ship steadily past the island, green and small, of the Sirens.

The polished oar blades dipped into the water without making a sound. Not even the slap of a wave against the prow broke the strange stillness.

Then, like a far-off echo in a dream, Ulysses heard a faint singing. The still air seemed to quiver as the thin, lovely sounds caressed his ears.

Ulysses took up a great block of beeswax from beneath one of the stern thwarts and went quickly toward the rowing benches. Heeding the sorceress' warning, he pinched off bits of the milky wax and pressed them into his companions' ears. His own ears he did not touch, for he was curious to hear the wonderful singing. But he had Eurylochus and another seaman tie him to the ship's mast. They bound their king so tightly that he could hardly move.

All the while the echoing music of the voices grew louder. Ulysses, the great fir-wood mast hard against his back, twisted his head toward the green island. It lay beneath a filmy haze, but he could see a meadow, shimmering with bright blossoms of blue and yellow and red. And now, as the sweet music swirled in the vibrant air, Ulysses could see the Sirens.

Two young and beautiful maidens sat in the midst of the flowers that covered the meadow. They turned their golden heads toward Ulysses and reached out their slim arms. Their honey-sweet voices fell upon the ears of long-suffering Ulysses like a mother's cool hand soothing the brow of a fevered child.

"Come," the voices sang, gentle in the misty air, "come, weary man, rest with us awhile." The very air seemed to smile, and the swaying flowers beckoned.

Ulysses strained eagerly against the ropes that held him. Ithaca was far away, and the voyage was hard and perilous. Who could tell if he might ever reach his home again? But here, right here, was a happy place, a place of dreams. He strained toward the lovely Sirens calling to him from their flowery meadow.

"Come, you are tired," their voices sang. "Come."

"Untie me!" Ulysses shouted. He twisted vainly, wrenching at the cords. "Polites! Eurylochus! Come loose me! I command you!"

But the rowers' ears were filled with wax, and they heard nothing, not the Sirens' song nor their king's helpless shouting. They rowed steadily on, past the island. The sea was calm and quiet, and the long oars lifted regularly in the air and plunged down again into the gray water, making barely a ripple.

Eurylochus turned his head as he rowed, and looked toward the little island. There seemed to be some sort of green meadow with flowers—but it was hazy, and he could not see very far into the island. What he could see on the shore, however, was clear enough. There was a great pile of whitened bones, lying amid jagged rocks.

Some poor seamen had run aground there, thought Eurylochus. A dangerous place. And he bent to his oar again.

The sea had come to life once more, and the wind blew fiercely, whipping the wave crests into foam. The crewmen, their ears emptied of wax, now shipped their oars and hoisted the broad sail. And then they saw the great rock.

No one could understand why they had not noticed it earlier. It stood up out of the gray sea like a fortress, like one of the walls of windy Troy. It stretched as far as they could see to either side, and its ends—if indeed it ended at all—were lost in mist and fog.

A beetling crag towered up in the center, directly in their path. Its top was buried in a black cloud. Against its base the wild surf crashed and thundered. And the wind now howled furiously over the little vessel, bellying out the white sail and driving the Greeks on swiftly.

"Take down the sail!" Ulysses commanded. The crew scrambled to obey him, but even when the tall mast was bare the vessel still flew before the gale. The surf boomed on the black rocks ahead. The spray leaped wildly.

Ulysses strained his eyes forward. As a giant breaker sent spume flying high up the cliff face, he thought he could glimpse a gap in the wall of rock. He seized the ship's tiller and steered in that direction.

Polites clambered toward him from the rowing benches. Salt spray glistened on the veteran captain's bald head as he leaned over to shout into his king's ear.

"A passage there—to the right of the peak!" He pointed to the place Ulysses had already seen, and the king of the Greeks nodded grimly in answer. The ship sped on.

Now the black cliff and its dark cloud loomed close. The blinding spray lashed them and darkened the air, but Ulysses kept his hand firmly on the tiller. Polites stood beside him, his feet braced wide on the slippery deck. The shadow of the crag was dark over the sea, and the crewmen held their breaths.

A great wave lifted them up, high amid the whipping spray. The little vessel seemed to balance on the wave crest, shaking itself. Ulysses could feel the tiller quivering under his hand. Then a fresh gust sent the ship heeling over on its side, and the tiller flew from Ulysses' grasp. The vessel swerved and drove straight for the cliff.

But Polites leaped upon the empty tiller and wrenched it over, turning the ship away from the looming rock. Then, between them, Polites and Ulysses held the tiller fast, steering the ship back toward the narrow gap in the cliff. As they strained over the tiller there was a final sea-surge, and the vessel, shuddering in a cloud of spume, raced safely into the passage.

To their left the cliff soared upward, smooth and black, its top lost in the dark cloud. To their right the crag was much lower, but just as steep. And between the two beetling cliffs ran a narrow corridor shadowed with mist. Far out ahead, Ulysses saw what looked like the gray of open water. At his command the crewmen began to row toward it. A strong current helped them, and the ship flew on eagerly.

They had almost reached the end of the narrow passage between the cliffs when a new sound was heard. The rowers twisted about on their benches and looked over their shoulders fearfully toward the strange hissing noise. At first all they could see was, atop the right-hand cliff, a massive fig tree bending its ancient and gnarled branches low toward the water. Then they saw what made the hissing noise.

They were being sucked straight into a spinning whirlpool. It seemed to stretch completely across the corridor. The black water swirled into foam as they watched. The foam raced in circles, swifter and swifter, and finally vanished into a spinning pit with no bottom. The current, powerful, relentless, was drawing the ship toward this deadly center.

"Hard over!" Ulysses cried. "There's a passage to the left!" And Polites helped him force the tiller over, both of them heaving mightily against the pull of the current. "Row! Pull!" Ulysses shouted, and the crewmen hauled at their oars. The whirlpool hissed and boiled.

But the red prow moved gradually to the left as the rowers fought the current. The towering cliff darkened the sky as they swept along beneath it. To their right, the wild whirlpool churned and seethed, tugging at the little vessel.

Then, above the hiss of the whirlpool, came the piercing sound of high-pitched yelping. Ulysses was reminded of a pack of hunting dogs circling about a wounded boar. The crewmen looked around in fright, and some of them almost lost their oars in the whirlpool.

The sounds came from the mouth of a cave in the cliff ahead of them to the left.

"By Zeus!" cried Polites. "What is that?"

"It must be the monster Scylla," replied Ulysses grimly. "The sorceress warned me—we must pass between a monster and a whirlpool."

"I see the whirlpool," said Polites, "but what is the monster like?"

Ulysses did not answer. Instead, he shouted to the crew, "Row! Row! Faster!"

The oarsmen strained, and the vessel shot forward, now hugging the cliff at the left, now being swept dangerously close to the black whirlpool at the right. The yelping sounds grew louder.

"What sort of monster?" Polites asked again.

Ulysses shrugged. "She said the whirlpool was deadlier," he answered. "Steer to the left!"

Polites obeyed, but glanced uneasily at the dark cave. They would pass directly under it, if the whirlpool did not suck them down first.

The Sacred Cattle

Later, when they had come safely out into the calm sea beyond, the men disagreed about what had really happened in the misty passage. Amid the spray and the weird yelping and the whirlpool's deafening hiss, no man could be certain of what he had seen. Some of them thought they had seen the wild face of a monster appear at the cave's edge as they went by. Others remembered a huge mouth gaping open to show rows of yellow teeth. Some had seen long arms reaching out of the cave. And there were even crewmen who thought they had seen three monsters, while others remembered five or six, or even a dozen.

But one thing they could all agree on, sadly. Their little ship held six fewer men now. Whatever they had seen in that moment of confusion and fright, they had all heard the screams of their comrades.

Ulysses himself could hardly believe what his eyes

had told him. It was a sight more terrible than anything he had faced in all his adventures.

He had seen a yelping monster with six heads. And he had seen this creature pluck six of his valiant crewmen from the ship and gobble them up, one in each set of snapping jaws.

Polites was among the six. As though in a nightmare, Ulysses had watched a long arm slide about the captain's waist like a snake and snatch him up, struggling and kicking, into the black cave. The last glimpse Ulysses had of his faithful comrade was just as the monster opened its vast jaws to devour him. And the last word he heard was an anguished scream: "Ulysses!"

Remembering now, as the ship rode gently on the open sea, the king of the Ithacans drew an unsteady hand across his eyes. Then he rose to his feet in the rocking vessel and looked at his companions. Some of them were still trembling; some of them wept.

"Hoist the sail," Ulysses commanded in a low voice. "Let us leave this evil place behind. I never want to behold it again."

There was really no need for them to stop at the next island. The wind held fair toward Ithaca, they had plenty of food and water, and there was no telling what dangers waited for them on the unknown shore. But Eurylochus, the last captain remaining to Ulysses now, looked around at the gathering twilight and urged that they land.

"Fierce winds are born at night," he said. "We would be safer ashore till morning." And from the crew came a deep-throated chorus of agreement.

"Listen!" Ulysses told them. He pointed a long arm toward the nearby island, which came closer every moment. "Listen! Even at this distance you can hear cattle lowing and sheep bleating. It is the island Circe warned me about—they are the flocks of the sun god."

"All the better," someone said. "Fresh meat."

"No!" Ulysses snapped. "The animals are sacred, and must not be touched. We will sail on."

But Eurylochus spoke again. "We are not all like you, exalted Ulysses," he said in bitterness. "You are stronger than other men. But we are tired, and sore at heart. A night ashore will refresh us."

"Aye!" the crewmen shouted. "A night on land!"

Ulysses scanned the island carefully before he spoke in return. Night was dropping close upon them, but finally the sharp-eyed Ithacan king saw a sheltered inlet between two green hills.

"Very well," Ulysses said, and the crewmen sighed with relief. But before they landed he made them swear an oath not to harm the sacred herds. "Ruin will come upon us all if you break this vow," the king warned as his men scrambled over the bulwarks and splashed ashore in the deepening twilight. The animals, beloved of the sun god, could be heard lowing contentedly on the hillsides.

"We sail away at dawn," said King Ulysses.

But fierce winds did indeed come that night, as Eurylochus had feared, and a storm raged all through the next morning. They dragged their long ship into a sheltered cave at the back of the inlet, and sat beside it on the floor of dry sand. At every lull in the storm, they could hear the cattle lowing outside.

Finally the storm was over, but it left the wrong wind behind. They were far out at the edge of the world, farther to the west than any men had ever been before, and they needed a wind that would carry them back. But the wind now blew only from the east, toward the unknown west, toward the outer darkness at the world's end.

They waited. Some days passed. They busied themselves about their ship, scraping the black sides and tightening the mast-stays and washing the sea wrack from the red-painted prow. When there was nothing more to be done they sat and waited again.

No new wind came to blow them home. A full month passed. A bubbling spring in the hillside gave them water, but their food was running low. Finally the last of it was eaten. They took to fishing, trailing sharp hooks of bronze in the gray sea about the island. Still the wind blew toward the west, away from Ithaca. They rubbed their empty stomachs and fished, but without much fortune. Near by, the cattle of the sun, the sacred cattle they had vowed not to touch, grazed peacefully.

"I shall be back soon," Ulysses said. He looked up

the hillside to where a clump of trees swayed and bent in the steady wind. "I go to pray to the gods for a west wind." Slowly he climbed the hill and disappeared over the crest. But before he was gone from the crew's sight he paused and looked back for a moment. Below him a few fat cattle stood in the shelter of a wind-ruffled tree. He pointed to them and called to his crewmen.

"Mind your oath!" he cried, and then walked away over the hilltop.

"Our oath!" Eurylochus said. "We shall die of hunger, and that will be the end of our oath!" He glared at the plump cows beneath the tree.

No one spoke. There was no sound but the sighing of the east wind and the lowing of the cattle. Then:

"Listen to me, all of you," said Eurylochus. "Do you want to starve to death?"

Returning, Ulysses smelled the roasting meat long before he came in sight of the beach. He paled, and groaned aloud.

"Father Zeus," he cried, "and all the blessed gods that be, have pity on us now for this monstrous deed." And he broke into a run, though he knew it was too late.

When he gained the crest of the hill and looked down upon the little camp, horror filled his heart. The crewmen had finished roasting the sacred cattle and were eating them greedily, squatting about the fire.

Ulysses stood motionless on the hilltop, in the wind.

Below him the carcasses of the slain cattle lay in pools of blood, dark on the yellow beach. As he gazed down now, it seemed to him that he stood again on the walls of windy Troy, watching vengeful Greeks slaughter Trojans amid the flames of the helpless city.

The fire crackled in the wind. Ulysses came down the hill slowly and joined his men. He scowled, but did not speak. There was nothing to say.

By the time the crewmen's stomachs were full, the wind had died down, for the first time in a month. Then it sprang up again, but now it blew toward the east, toward home. Eagerly the Greeks scrambled aboard their black ship and pushed off. They set the fir-wood mast in its socket and hoisted the white sail, and soon the island of the sun god's sacred cattle was gone from view.

No other land appeared. The little vessel was alone on the vast sea, under the sunless sky. Ulysses sat on the stern deck, his back against the rail, and searched the eastern horizon. Beside him the helmsman plied the tiller. On the rowing benches the crewmen rested upon their shipped oars and listened to the voice of Eurylochus. He was telling them about the temple they would build to appease the sun god when they reached Ithaca.

Suddenly the sky darkened. The wind began to rise, and the crew stirred themselves to take down the flapping sail. The sea grew black. The sky had now turned dark as night.

Then a mighty blast of wind hit them like a hammer blow. The mast bent far over, and then cracked, and finally broke off at its base. It toppled into the ship, ropes and stays flying wildly. Ulysses saw the helmsman killed beside him, his skull crushed by the falling mast.

Now a thunderbolt, crackling and huge, struck the rowing benches. A greenish-white light dazzled Ulysses' eyes, and sulphurous smoke burned his nostrils. The slender ship quivered like a falling leaf. Then a giant wave crashed down, and then another, and then the vessel began to break apart.

The crewmen were swept into the churning sea, and Ulysses saw them no more. Quickly now, one hand grasping the shattered rail, he cut the oxhide stays away from the mast with his dagger of bronze. Then he threw himself across the heavy mast and clung to it as the sea pounded his ship to splinters.

A final angry wave sent the mast flying through a swirl of wreckage and spray and choking salt water. Ulysses shut his eyes and held on as the sea closed over his head. The mast slowly rolled him to the surface again, and he was able to gulp a huge mouthful of air. Then another black wave smothered him. Ulysses held on to the fir-wood mast with all his strength, and he prayed.

All day and all night the furious wind and the waves bore Ulysses along. When dawn came at last, he lifted his head and looked about in the early light.

His fingers were cramped and stiff, and salt water streamed down his face, burning his eyes.

Directly before him, looming closer every moment, were the familiar black cliff and the giant fig tree that bent out over the water. And now he heard the terrible hissing of the whirlpool Charybdis. He was being swept straight toward it.

This time there was no escape. Helpless in the grip of the current, with no way of steering, Ulysses was sucked into the spinning black pit like a twig being carried over a mountain waterfall.

But the man of many wiles was not lost yet. At the very last instant, when he was almost engulfed by the swirling currents at the whirlpool's center, he let go of the water-logged mast. Raising his arms high above his head, he seized a low branch of the ancient fig tree. The mast—all that was left of his proud black ship—rolled and spun and then vanished into the racing center of the whirlpool.

Ulysses was left clinging to the fig tree, water pouring from him. The whirlpool tugged at his ankles, but he did not let go, even though the sandals were torn from his feet and his body was twisted halfway round by the spinning waters. He did not let go, although his fingers grew cramped and swollen, and his arms and shoulders ached.

The fig tree dipped low under his weight, and the sucking water pulled and twisted him, but the great-hearted king of Ithaca held on. His fingers, and then

Ulysses was left clinging to the fig tree

his arms, grew numb; sharp pains seared his back and shoulders; the whirlpool hissed and boiled and tugged; but he held on.

He held on so tightly that the branches cut his hands, and warm, sticky blood ran down his arms. He gritted his teeth and shut his eyes. The steady hissing filled his ears.

Then suddenly the whirlpool changed its sound. The hissing died away and became a bubbling, and then a roar. Ulysses opened his eyes and looked down.

The sorceress had told the truth. The whirlpool was no longer tugging at his ankles; instead it was spewing up from its black center great patches of foam and dead fig leaves and broken tree branches. A spar from some ill-fated ship came to the surface as Ulysses watched, and he saw it sweep to the edge of the whirlpool and float out to sea.

And then at last his own fir-wood mast came into view. Ulysses dropped into the water with a splash and clutched the great pole with swollen, numb fingers. It rolled and pitched, but when Ulysses dared to raise his streaming head from the water he saw that he was being carried out to sea again.

He gripped the mast tighter and tried to smile through his cracked lips. The salt sea washed over his head. He closed his eyes.

The Offer of a Goddess

Now Ulysses seemed to be in a little brook that gurgled and splashed. He felt himself floating along gently, warmed by the sun. The sun was friendly, welcome. He had not seen it since leaving Troy a long time ago.

And now birds were flying about, bringing him food in their beaks. He could hear them chattering and chirping. The food smelled delicious, and he tried to reach out for it.

"No, no," a soft voice said, "lie still. There . . . are you awake now?" A warm hand touched his forehead.

He opened his eyes. He was lying on his back, looking up at a smiling, yellow-haired woman who sat bending over him. A big red bird swept up, fluttering its wings and squawking, and landed on her shoulder.

Ulysses struggled to his elbows, blinking in the light. He lay on a patch of green grass at the mouth of a cave. Birds flew back and forth overhead, and the air was heavy with the fragrance of flowers. The sun had shone, alas, only in his dream, but the hazy air was still warm.

Beyond the smiling woman he saw a row of four large fountains, gurgling and splashing peacefully. Now the red bird spread its brilliant wings and flew from the woman's shoulder. Ulysses watched it swoop low over the fountains, and then soar across a broad meadow filled with violets, and disappear into a clump of tall trees in the distance. Beyond the trees Ulysses could make out the gray sea.

"I was shipwrecked in a storm," he said, leaning back and closing his eyes again, remembering.

"Yes," the woman said. "You are safe now."

"Were none of my comrades washed ashore with me?" he asked, his eyes still shut.

"No," she answered, "just you, Ulysses."

He opened his eyes with a start. "You know my name?"

She nodded. "I know all about you, King of Ithaca. You have endured much in your travels, but now you will rest."

Ulysses smiled. "If you know all this, you must be no ordinary woman," he said, half joking. "You must be a goddess."

"Yes," she said simply. "I am the goddess Calypso."

She said no more after that, but fed the hungry Ulysses and then let him sleep. Later they sat in the doorway of the cave and talked together, the goddess and the mortal king. Dusk had fallen, and the tall trees at the shore were black against the gray sky of twilight. A fire crackled and flamed near the four fountains. The sweet scent of juniper and cedar and violets filled the air, along with smoke from the fire and the rustling of the swift birds. There was a breeze, gentle and cool on Ulysses' forehead.

Calypso talked of the gods, and of her peaceful green island, and of what it meant to be immortal. Ulysses spoke of his home.

It was the first of a great many such evenings, for the goddess Calypso quickly found that she had fallen in love with red-haired Ulysses, even though she was a goddess and he a mortal man. She desired him for a husband.

When he was rested, Ulysses was eager to be on his way again, but Calypso forced him to stay. She was a powerful goddess, far more powerful than any earthly king, and Ulysses could make her do nothing against her will. She would not let him leave the island.

"Stay here with me and be happy," she implored him, stroking his shoulder with her white hand. "I will make you immortal. Do you not want to live forever? Think of it, Ulysses—you could do what no man has ever done. You could ignore death."

Ulysses said nothing, but he thought of his brave comrades who had died at Troy and on the island of the Cyclops and on the terrible sea. He thought of Eurybates and Polites and Eurylochus, and of all the other Greeks who had died trying to sail home to Ithaca. He sniffed the gentle air of Calypso's isle, scented with violets and cedar, and he looked out at the sea, cold, cruel, vast. The goddess' offer was tempting.

But something else came into his mind, too. He saw the green forests and white houses of Ithaca, and he remembered the way smoke rose up to the sky from the hearth fires. He saw his own hearth fire, with his father and mother beside it, and his wife Penelope and his son Telemachus.

"You have wandered a long time," Calypso said, caressing his scarred hands. "Rest now, Ulysses."

"Aye," he said, "I have wandered long. It is time I returned to my own home, and my family."

The goddess spoke no more. But her hand still caressed him, and she smiled to herself. She was a goddess; she was powerful. She knew that mortal men forget, and she could wait.

She waited seven years. Ulysses refused to forget his home. He took the tall fir-wood mast upon which he had been washed ashore, and he planted it erect in the beach, to remind him of his ship and of Ithaca, where it had been made. Each morning, when he awoke in Calypso's lofty cave, he rose and went down across the violet-filled meadow to the beach. Each evening the goddess found him there, sitting with his back against the sturdy mast, gazing out to sea.

She would lead him back to the cave, but as he went he would turn his head and look at the tall mast, black in the twilight. The goddess knew she was defeated.

"A raft!" Ulysses said. He shook his head sadly. "I have thought of it a thousand times, but I have no tools to build one."

The goddess Calypso sighed. "I will give you all the tools you need," she said, "if you really want them." She looked out at the sea for a moment. "Last night," she said, "I was spoken to by Hermes, the messenger of the gods. They have decreed that I should set you free."

Ulysses said nothing, but his heart pounded. There was a silence.

Calypso sighed again. Then she took Ulysses by the chin and forced him to look into her eyes.

"Look at me," she said. "Is your Penelope so much prettier than I?"

Ulysses took her hand from his chin and held it. "Goddess," he said gently, "no mortal woman could be as beautiful as you, who are ageless. But would you keep me from my home and my own family?"

"The sea is perilous, Ulysses, between here and your Ithaca. Poseidon the Earth-Shaker is your deadly enemy."

"Even so," said Ulysses, "I must try. My duty lies in Ithaca. If Poseidon strikes at me on the way, I shall endure it."

The goddess brought him tools the next day. When the first rosy fingers of dawn appeared in the eastern sky, she put a great ax into Ulysses' hands. His eyes widened in surprise; it was a Greek ax, with an olive-wood shaft and a heavy blade of iron pierced with a round hole. Ulysses gripped the smooth handle in both hands and hefted the ax. He grinned with pleasure at the feel of it, his white teeth gleaming in his tanned face.

Calypso, beautiful in a golden-belted robe, walked with him to the clump of tall trees that stood near the shore. Ulysses lifted the pierced ax from his shoulder and began to fell a straight poplar. The steady blows sounded in the goddess' ears as she walked back to the cave.

In all, Ulysses cut down twenty trees, poplar and alder and fir. He trimmed them and smoothed them, working swiftly. Calypso brought him augers, and he bored holes so that he might fasten the beams together with heavy whittled pegs. He fitted enough timbers side by side to make a broad deck, and upon this he fastened stout beams as cross-ribs. Around the edges of the close-set deck he built gunwales, and along them he fastened willow withes and brush to break the force of the waves.

The sea pounded the nearby shore, as it had for seven long years, but he heard it not. Nor did he hear the inquisitive birds fluttering and screeching about him. He was too busy now. He was building a vessel to take him home to Ithaca at last.

On the fourth day the raft was finished, and lay on the wet, dark sand at the edge of the beach. He had made a long steering oar and he had set up a

tall mast, well braced, with a yardarm fitted to it. Calypso had given him enough finely woven cloth to make a sail.

Ulysses slept in the fragrant cave for the last time that night. When dawn came the goddess woke him and walked by his side down to the beach, through the violet-meadow wet with dew. The warm air was just coming alive with bird song.

Ulysses put a great wineskin aboard the raft. He took another skin filled with fresh water, and loaded a big sack with food. Calypso watched him quietly. She stood leaning against the tall black mast that the king of Ithaca had set upright in the beach seven years before—the fir-wood mast that had brought him to her island.

She stood by it while he thanked her, bade her a tender farewell, and set sail. She stood by it as the little raft moved swiftly out upon the wide sea, and for a long time Ulysses sat looking back at the tall black mast and the white-robed goddess beside it. But finally they dropped from sight, and then the island itself disappeared below the horizon. Ulysses of the steadfast heart was alone on the gray sea again.

For seventeen days he enjoyed fair winds. The raft steered well and took the rolling waves easily. On the morning of the eighteenth day, land came into sight. Ulysses saw shadowy mountains rising up slowly out of the dark sea. The mountains were none he had ever seen before, but he steered for them and watched them grow larger on the horizon.

Then the storm struck. The raft was well made; it survived the first attack of the furious wind and the smashing waves, although the mast was snapped in two and the steering oar was swept away. Ulysses crawled to the center of the raft and clung there. The foaming seas broke angrily over his head. The sky grew black; the wind howled.

A wave greater than any before arched up over the raft, spume blowing from its crest. It towered higher, gathered force, and then came thundering down, smashing the raft to splinters. The massive timbers, hewn so carefully, were scattered like wisps of straw.

The black waters closed over Ulysses, but he fought his way back up to the surface and raised his head into the air. The slashing water blinded him as he gasped for breath. Finally, lifted by a wave, he caught a glimpse of the gray mountains again. When the wave dashed him back down, he began to swim toward the land.

He swam for two whole days and nights. The gods had given Ulysses strength in great measure, and he used it now. He swam grimly, steadily, buffeted by the waves but always keeping the mountains in sight. His arms and legs and head ached, and the salt water burned his eyes, but he swam on.

He reached the land at last, but he found no beach where he could go ashore. Instead, there were jagged reefs, evil looking, on which the sea pounded wildly. His strength was almost all gone now, and he swam slowly, in great pain. The sea swept him against the reefs, and the sharp rocks cut his swollen hands. The salt burned cruelly in the wounds.

The sea swept him out again, and this time he managed to swim along the reefs, looking for a passage to the land. He swam wearily, at the end of his strength. He could see nothing but the churning foam, and everywhere the black reefs. Were his travels to end now, here in the dark sea?

Then suddenly he came to a river mouth, and an opening in the reefs.

After what seemed a long time he crawled feebly ashore. Blindly, painfully, the king of Ithaca dragged his swollen body up along the river bank and into a clump of bushes. Behind him the breakers pounded the reefs, as though angry at his escape.

He pulled a thornbush aside with bleeding hands, and collapsed into a heap of dead leaves.

The Greatest Sailors in the World

The Princess Nausicaa, daughter of King Alcinous of Phaeacia, rose from her bed early, in the first light of dawn. Though she was the daughter of a king, Nausicaa sometimes liked to go with her handmaidens to the washing place at the river.

The day was growing warm as Nausicaa, sitting high on the seat of a mule wagon piled with soiled clothes, made her way out of the palace gates. The handmaidens ran chattering alongside. The gray mules hauled the wagon, creaking and jouncing, down the road toward the sea that surrounded the island of Phaeacia.

At the washing pits near the river mouth, the maidens unloaded the wagon. Nausicaa sat on the wagon seat, her elbows on her knees and her chin in her hands, and daydreamed. She tried to imagine the day

—not far off, she hoped—when some young Phaeacian nobleman would ask for her hand in marriage. What would he look like?

When the washing was finished, and the clothes were all spread out to dry upon the pebbles of the shore, the princess and her maidens ate their midday meal. They sat beside the wagon, while a warm sea breeze ruffled the bushes at the nearby river mouth. On the sea the waves rolled evenly, breaking in long lines of white foam far out on the reefs.

After eating, they leaped to their feet and played a game. They threw a bright yellow ball back and forth along the beach, jumping high in the warm air and laughing and singing. Nausicaa led the song in her clear young voice.

There was a chorus of screams as the ball sailed over a maiden's clutching fingers and disappeared into the bushes. Three girls ran to get it. Nausicaa yawned, and stretched her white arms in the breeze.

There was a scream—a real one this time. The maidens came running back to Nausicaa, their eyes wide with fright. The princess looked toward the bushes, and she saw what had frightened them.

A man was staggering toward her. His eyes and hair were wild; his clothes were ragged shreds. Now he stopped and watched the terrified handmaidens scurry back to the shelter of the wagon. Nausicaa, the daughter of King Alcinous, was left alone facing the man. She did not move, but stood looking at him, her head held high.

The man was not tall, but he had a broad chest and thick, heavy shoulders. He swayed a little on his feet. Dead leaves stuck to his legs, and his red hair and beard were matted with sea salt.

I must not be afraid, thought Nausicaa. She wanted to turn her head and look for her maidens, but she could not move.

There was silence. Nausicaa's heart pounded wildly. Then the man cleared his throat, tried to smile with his cracked, salt-caked lips, and finally spoke.

When the words came they were very soft and gentle. "Are you a goddess?" the man asked. The girl did not answer, and he smiled at her and said, "Surely you are as fair as a goddess—but if you are a mortal woman, then how fortunate your parents are. And how fortunate will be the man who wins you over and has you for his wife."

Nausicaa's cheeks colored a little, but she said nothing. "Please forgive me for appearing before you this way," said the red-haired man, "but I have been many days alone in the sea, and Poseidon of the great storms has not been kind to me." He smiled again. "I have been shipwrecked, and I have been much afraid, but I see now that I have come to a land of kind and gentle folk."

Nausicaa found her voice at last. It wavered just a little as she spoke. "If—if you are alone and in need," she said, "you have no reason to be afraid now. I—my father, that is—will help you. He is king here."

Ulysses breathed a great sigh, and smiled more broadly. "Tell me, Princess," he said, "what place is this?"

"It is called Phaeacia . . . but we must give you some food and clothing now." Nausicaa turned and called to her handmaidens cowering by the mule wagon. "Why do you run at the sight of a man?" she demanded sharply. "It is nothing to be afraid of —now come bring him some food. Hurry!"

When he had eaten, the maidens showed Ulysses a place behind the bushes at the river's edge where he might bathe in privacy. They waited as he washed the sea-scurf and grime from his weary body. He dressed himself in a tunic and cloak that the handmaidens left beside the bushes, and then he came out and faced them. This time they did not run away.

At twilight that evening, Ulysses ate at a banquet in the royal palace of King Alcinous. He sat on a silver-studded chair beside the king, leaning against one of the great pillars of the palace eating hall. Torches blazed all about, sending smoke up to the high-vaulted ceiling. Noblemen of the kingdom of Phaeacia filled the hall, talking, laughing, eating. They sat on backless chairs and benches or reclined on curved couches, and they ate from little polished tables drawn up close to them. Pages hurried back and forth in the flickering torchlight, carrying silver platters of meats and fresh bread, pouring dark wine into the golden mixing bowls.

"Tell me, Princess," he said, "what place is this?"

Queen Arete had already finished eating, and sat idly winding a ball of rich purple yarn. She smiled and chatted with the royal guests, but from time to time her eyes fell upon the quiet red-bearded stranger who sat beside Alcinous.

The Princess Nausicaa sat by her mother on a low stool. She too let her eyes stray toward the stranger. Her mother noticed, and smiled.

When all the guests had eaten their fill, a royal herald entered, leading a blind minstrel, an old man clad in a white robe. The herald set a chair, bright with silver nails, against a pillar for him, and put his shining lyre on a peg near by.

As the servant guided the minstrel's hands to where the lyre hung, King Alcinous spoke out, his voice echoing in the lofty hall.

"Demodocus," he said, "honored of the gods, what tale will you tell us this evening?"

The minstrel turned his sightless eyes toward the sound of his king's voice. He smiled, and bowed his white head gravely. "Good King Alcinous has been kind to me in my days here," he said in answer. "I am grateful. Shall I sing now of the love between Ares, the god of war, and Aphrodite, goddess of love?"

"Yes!" the guests cried in delight. And blind Demodocus, to whom the gods had sent the gift of sweet song in return for his lost sight, stroked the silver lyre and began. He sang a story in song about some of the immortal gods dwelling high on Mount Olympus. It was not a long tale, but it was a lovely one, and the hall fell into a deep silence after the minstrel had plucked the last clear note on his gleaming lyre.

Queen Arete broke the silence. She looked directly toward the newcomer and said, "Perhaps now, stranger, you will tell us who you are and whence you have come to our island."

Ulysses told them. He closed his eyes for a moment first and gave thanks to the immortal gods that he was safe again, and rested, and fed. Then he opened his eyes and thanked King Alcinous and Queen Arete, and the charming Princess Nausicaa, for their kindness to him. He smiled a little as the princess lowered her eyes, and then he took a deep breath and began his story.

He had not realized how much had happened to him since he left Ithaca for Troy, almost twenty years before. But he told everything, beginning with the day when he stood on the beach at Ithaca, bidding farewell to his wife Penelope and their son Telemachus. When he mentioned his wife, young Nausicaa sighed and looked up at her mother. The queen patted her daughter's hand. A smile touched the corners of Ulysses' mouth and deep-set eyes, but he spoke on.

He told of the long war at far-off Troy, and of the trick by which it was finally won in the tenth year. He spoke of the hollow wooden horse, and of the

The banqueters listened with wonder to every word

Greek soldiers pouring through the open gates of the sleeping city—and then his smooth voice changed and faltered.

Hoarsely, brokenly, Ulysses said, "Our men slaughtered the Trojans like animals. The war was too long and too bitter, and they lost control of themselves at the end. The gods above must have been horrified And then his voice stopped altogether.

The royal family and their guests all waited in lence. Ulysses sat with his head bent and his han over his eyes. At last he raised his head. Tears glis tened on his cheeks.

"I have always known," he said slowly, "that the gods give us two portions of woe for every portion of joy. I have always known that. But I think this was something more. I sailed for home with twelve good ships, filled with riches and with my faithful comrades—and I sit before you now with empty hands, alone, a wanderer. All of my comrades are dead, and perhaps the gods will take my life too, ere I see Ithaca again. Aye, the gods are angry, and vengeful."

There was another silence. "Well," Ulysses said at last, "they have good reason to be angry." And he sighed heavily and took up his story once more.

It was a marvelous tale indeed, and the banqueters in the palace of rich King Alcinous listened

He told of Polites being devoured by the monster

with wonder to every word. Their eyes opened wide when Ulysses spoke of the strange lotus blossom, the flower of forgetfulness. They gasped when he described the man-eating Cyclops, with the single great eye in the center of his forehead. They groaned when he told them how, within sight of Ithaca, the foolish crewmen had opened the bag of winds.

The noble guests squirmed uneasily on their cushioned chairs at the story of Circe turning men into swine. They sighed at poor Elpenor's death. They leaned forward breathlessly as the little band of Greeks rowed their vessel through the passage between deadly Scylla and the terrible whirlpool Charybdis. They shuddered at the picture of brave Polites being devoured by the monster; they could hear him screaming "Ulysses!" as the black ship swept on.

The long-suffering king of Ithaca left nothing out of the story. Ten years of war and ten years of wandering. And was he any nearer to his home now, after all these years?

He was nearer than he thought. For when Ulysses had at last finished his long tale, and sat with head bowed, King Alcinous and all the nobles in the great hall rose to their feet and vowed to outfit a stout fifty-oared ship to take the wanderer home.

They kept their vow. One day not long afterward, a smiling, rested, and grateful Ulysses walked from the royal palace down to the shore where the long ship and its fifty oarsmen waited. By chance, young

Nausicaa was leaning against a doorpost in the palace entrance as he passed.

"Farewell, King Ulysses. I hope you will not forget us when you reach your native land."

Ulysses stopped before her. "Princess," he said, "you will be in my prayers always. I owe my life to you." He leaned forward and took her white hand in his scarred brown one. "If I reach my home again——"

"You will reach Ithaca safely," Nausicaa said. "You must not worry. The Phaeacians are the greatest sailors in the world."

Ulysses smiled. "That may be," he said, "but I think that if I reach my home it will be because the gods decide I have suffered enough." He released her hand. "But whatever the gods have in store for me," he said, "I shall never forget King Alcinous and Queen Arete—and their lovely daughter."

The princess and Ulysses looked into each other's eyes for a moment. Then Ulysses turned away and strode down to the waiting ship and the gray, sunless sea.

A House Full of Enemies

Prince Telemachus, tall and fair, stood on the beach at Ithaca with the brilliant sun beating down on his head. He watched the sea—the unresting sea that rolled, blue and sparkling, upon the shore of Ithaca. The sea was empty. No white sail showed on the horizon; no vessel approached that might bring the prince news of his father—or, better still, that might bring him Ulysses himself after all these years. Sometimes Telemachus felt that the dark sea was his enemy.

If so, it was not his only enemy. The young prince shook his head angrily and said aloud, "It is not fair! There are too many!"

"Too many what, my lord?" a voice said at his elbow.

He turned and saw old Eumaeus, the palace swineherd, his father's faithful servant. "You know well," Telemachus said to the old man. "Too many suitors for my mother's hand. They all hope that my father is dead, and they flock around like vultures to put their claws on his queen."

"And on his palace and its treasure room," Eumaeus added.

Telemachus smiled bitterly as his eyes swept the horizon. "Well," he said, "there will soon be very little treasure left for them. They have been feasting and partying for three years now in my father's halls, pouring his wealth down their greedy gullets. How much longer can we pay for it?"

"My finest pigs have all been eaten long since," the swineherd said.

"And we can do nothing!" said Telemachus. "Nothing!" He kicked the sand moodily. "We are helpless against all these suitors. We can only watch the sea, and hope my father will return."

Eumaeus looked at the prince keenly. "My lord," he said, "there is a man at my hut now—a traveler——"

Telemachus clutched the old man's shoulder. "He has news of my father?"

"Well—perhaps if you were to question him——"

But already Telemachus was striding off eagerly toward the swineherd's hut. The old man labored after him. He did not even glance at the sea as he went.

Telemachus was breathing hard from his climb when he entered the hut. A bearded stranger rose from a pile of shaggy gray goatskins in one corner.

In the half-light, Telemachus saw a man not tall but powerfully built, with massive shoulders and arms. His hands were large, gnarled, scarred—the hands of a sailor, Telemachus decided. And his thick legs were a little bowed, like a sailor's.

The stranger stepped slowly forward. His red hair and beard glinted in the light from the doorway. His face was lined and weather-beaten. Deep-set gray eyes studied Telemachus for a moment, and then the man bowed his head slightly.

"Greetings, O Prince," he said. His voice was deep.

Telemachus cleared his throat. "You are welcome here, sir," he said, trying to match the stranger's commanding voice. "Please sit down. Have you eaten?"

The stranger nodded. "Your swineherd has been kind to me. I wish I might reward him."

"He will be happy enough if you bring news of his master," Telemachus said. "And so will I. But please be seated, sir, and let us speak in comfort. Have you traveled a great distance?"

The stranger turned and went toward the couch of goatskins. *This is no ordinary seaman,* thought Telemachus. *He moves like a king.*

The bearded man sat, and gazed up at Telemachus for a long moment. The prince saw the gray eyes rake him from head to toe.

"You have traveled far?" Telemachus asked again.

"From Troy."

"Troy! Were you in the war there? Did you know Ulysses, my father?"

The stranger seemed to hesitate; then he nodded. "Yes, I knew your father well."

Telemachus rushed forward eagerly, his princely bearing all forgotten now. "When did you last see him? Is he alive?"

"If he were alive," asked the stranger, "would you recognize him?"

Telemachus considered for a moment. "I do not know," he said slowly. "I was a baby when he left for the war. But my mother has told me what he looked like. If he has not changed too much in twenty years, I think I might know him."

The stranger smiled. "Twenty years is a long time. I think he has changed a great deal."

Telemachus' eyes widened. "Then he is alive?"

The stranger did not answer, but asked a question instead: "Have you courage, Prince?"

The young man flushed deeply. "I have never been in battle," he replied, "but I think my father would not be ashamed of me."

A shadow fell across Telemachus' face. He turned; the old swineherd Eumaeus stood in the sunny doorway, smiling. Then, from the pile of goatskins in the corner, Telemachus heard the stranger's deep voice.

"Go, Eumaeus," the voice said. "Go to your herds. Leave me with my son."

The swineherd stood there for an instant, taking pleasure in the wide-eyed look of surprise and unbelieving joy on his young prince's face. Then he turned and left the hut. He stretched his old arms in the fine hot sun as he went, and he grinned to himself.

When Eumaeus returned to the hut the father and son were already deep in plans. They sat side by side on the shaggy couch of skins; Ulysses had a long arm about Telemachus' shoulders. The young man raised a happy face, stained with tears, as the swineherd entered. "Why did you not tell me, Eumaeus?"

The old man chuckled. "Would you have me take from my king the joy of telling you himself? He came yesterday, straight to my dwelling. A god must have brought him here!"

"He is right, Father," said Telemachus. "If you had gone first to the palace, the suitors might have recognized you and killed you."

"Aye, the suitors," said Ulysses thoughtfully. "Tell me, how does your mother feel about these men who want to marry her?"

Eumaeus snorted. "How do we *all* feel about them! We would like to see them dead, every last one."

"And how many are there of these men?" asked Ulysses.

"Many, many," said Telemachus. "Past counting."

"A hundred and eight," said Eumaeus.

"Father," Telemachus said, "I will show you how my mother feels about them. Three years ago, when they began banqueting and feasting in the palace——"

"They were certain you were dead, sire," put in Eumaeus.

"Yes, and nothing could drive them from our

house," said Telemachus. "They insisted that my mother choose one of them for her new husband. She finally agreed, but told them that first she had to finish the burial robe she was weaving for your father, Laertes, against the day when death takes him."

"How is my father?" asked Ulysses.

Telemachus hesitated, then said, "You know that your mother is dead? She died of grief, Father, longing for your return."

Ulysses nodded slowly. "Eumaeus told me."

"Well," said Telemachus, "Grandfather Laertes still lives, but he is bowed down with unhappiness. He never comes to the palace now, but stays on his farm."

Ulysses sighed. "And your mother weaves him a burial robe."

"Every day," said Telemachus, "the suitors would see her working at it, and they would think she was a day closer to marrying one of them." Telemachus leaned forward, his eyes flashing. "And every night she would unravel most of what she had done during the day! That is how she feels about the suitors, Father!"

"It was a good trick," said Eumaeus, "but they found out at last."

Telemachus sank back. "Yes," he said morosely.

Ulysses looked at his son. "Eumaeus told me that these suitors had a plan to kill you, but it failed," he said.

Telemachus frowned darkly. "They lay in ambush to murder me," he said, "but I was warned, and escaped." He clenched his fists. "One day they will pay for it!"

"Yes, I think they will," said Ulysses quietly. He tightened his arm about his son's shoulders. "And you will not have to face them all alone now." Father and son smiled at each other.

"But there are many against us," said Ulysses, "and we need to be careful. You must tell no one I am home, not even your mother! Meanwhile, we will continue with our plans."

The long-suffering king of Ithaca rose to his feet. "First," he said, "I would like to see these intruders for myself."

The beggar paused a moment before entering the palace courtyard. He squinted up at the high marble walls gleaming in the afternoon sun. Then he passed through the gate, hobbling slowly, leaning on his stick. His dirty cloak was full of holes; his feet were bare.

"Do you want food, old man?" asked a palace servant, watching him.

The beggar nodded his dusty head. He held out a pouch of worn leather hanging from his shoulder on a frayed and many-knotted cord.

The servant jerked a thumb toward the palace. "They've got plenty of food in there," he said. "You can hear them enjoying it." From the great hall of the palace came music and gay shouts and the clank of metal goblets.

"A feast?" muttered the old man.

"Aye, a feast," the palace servant said bitterly. "They're feasting on another man's wine and meat—and they want his queen, too." He spat angrily into the dust. "Ah, but if my master were only here—a fine feast he'd give them!"

The beggar said nothing. He bent over his staff and raised an arm, trembling with age, to point. "Is that your dog?"

The servant turned and looked at an old hound that lay feebly panting in the sun. At the sound of the beggar's voice, the old dog pricked up his ears and tried to wag his tail.

"That's old Argus," the palace servant answered. "He was a great dog once. But now his good master, King Ulysses, lies dead far away somewhere." He shook his head. "These are sad days. But go, old man, ask for food in the hall there."

The servant trotted off. The beggar stood with tears in his eyes, watching as the faithful dog Argus struggled weakly to run to his master one last time—struggled, rose to his feet, panted happily, and then slumped over, dead.

Clutching his beggar's disguise about his bent shoulders, Ulysses shuffled to the door of his palace. Painfully, like a stiff-jointed old man, he eased himself down to the stone threshold and sat leaning back against the doorpost. He turned his dirt-smeared face and looked into the great hall.

A double row of pillars, of white and blue-veined marble, stretched from the doorway back to the far end of the vast hall. Ulysses let his eyes move slowly down the long line of pillars, to rest on the staircase leading up to the other rooms of the palace. He saw Prince Telemachus sitting quietly on a chair near the foot of the stairs. There was no sign of Penelope.

But there were other things for his eyes to see, in this first glimpse of his home in twenty years. There were perhaps a hundred men lolling about in the hall, on chairs, benches, couches, or the floor. Some were eating, while servants hurried back and forth with trays of steaming meats and bowls of wine. Some were gambling: the sharp cries of the players rose over the general noise. Some argued, some danced gaily, some were already groggy with wine.

A group near Ulysses sang a raucous drinking song, with silver goblets—*his* goblets—held high. One of the

The old dog tried to wag his tail

singers, red-faced, fumbled drunkenly for a wine bowl on a low table and upset table and bowl and all. His friends roared with laughter.

Ulysses watched the dark stain of the wine spread across the white marble floor of his palace, and he thought: *These are the men who tried to kill my son. These are the men who drove my father into a life of misery. These are the men who want my wife.*

He heaved himself to his feet and began to beg for food. He shuffled slowly about the hall, holding out his worn leather bag for scraps of meat or bread.

"Antinous!" someone called loudly near Ulysses. "Ho, Antinous!"

At the sound of this name, the noise seemed to lessen a bit. Then a tall man, blond and clean-shaven, rose to his feet on the other side of the hall and shouted, "Quiet!" The revelers fell silent.

"What is it?" demanded the blond Antinous.

"Just a beggar," said the man near Ulysses. "He has something to say to you." And, laughing, he put a hand on Ulysses' back and pushed him violently forward toward the man called Antinous. "Beg from Lord Antinous, old man. He is kind to beggars!" And he bellowed with laughter, slapping his thigh mightily.

Antinous scowled. "Keep him away from me. You know how I hate beggars."

But Ulysses of the many wiles decided to shamble forward, his leather bag held out toward the suitor

Antinous. "It is no man's fault to be a beggar, sire," he said in a cracked and wavering voice. "I was a rich man like yourself before the gods sent misfortune down on me." He held up his grimy bag, showing a few bits of meat. "I have nothing but this now, while you have plenty of good food and wine, and a marble hall to eat in. Surely you can spare just a little of your food." There was a chorus of laughs from the other suitors.

Antinous' face grew dark below his blond hair, and he fingered the bronze sword that hung at his side. "Begone, vile old man!" he snapped. "I have nothing for you!"

But Ulysses did not move. "You have such a fine place here," he said. The suitors roared at the joke. "Give me just a morsel," Ulysses pleaded.

"I'll give you a morsel!" Antinous screamed. "There, eat that!" And he snatched up a wooden footstool and heaved it at Ulysses' head.

Still the king in beggar's rags did not move. The stool caught him high on the shoulder, and rebounded to the marble floor with a loud clatter.

Young Telemachus sprang up, his eyes blazing.

Penelope

Quickly Ulysses shook his head and darted a warning look at his son. Telemachus stopped, and bit his lips, and then slowly returned to his seat.

Ulysses said no more. He shuffled awkwardly back to the threshold and sat down. Antinous had forgotten him already; he was helping himself to bread and meat from a platter held by a servant. At the threshold of the palace King Ulysses picked a scrap of gristly meat from his bag on the floor beside him. The gay party continued.

Now a servant bent over Ulysses. "Old man," he said, "come with me. Queen Penelope would question you."

Ulysses finished the offering he was making to the immortal gods—a bit of meat set aside from the few pieces in his pouch—and then he raised his head and heaved himself slowly erect. Following the servant, he hobbled through the hall. He was a beggar, tattered, feeble, and old. None of the banqueters paid him any heed.

At the top of the staircase, the king of Ithaca paused and looked down at the scene in the dining hall of his palace. A mock battle had begun; the drunken revelers were pelting each other with chunks of bread and meat. Screams of laughter filled the hall. Directly below Ulysses sat Prince Telemachus, stiff and unsmiling. The king in beggar's rags watched his son for a moment. Then he turned and followed the servant to Queen Penelope's chamber.

"Enter," the queen called. They went in. Ulysses' heart gave a leap as he saw a slim figure, robed in blue, standing at a far window. Her dark hair hung down her back, shining in the sunset that lit her face and white arms. She was looking out to sea, to the east, toward Troy.

Finally she turned to face Ulysses, and said, "Please sit down, good sir." Her voice was soft. "Eury-clea, give our guest a chair."

An old woman at the side of the room straightened up from her sewing and looked at Ulysses sharply. "Sit there, old man," she said, pointing to a low wooden bench, its yellow paint cracked and flaking. "It belonged to the child Ulysses, when I was his nurse. Sit on the king's bench, old man, and weave us a tale of lies about his return." She glared at Ulysses.

"Be quiet, woman," said Penelope. She came forward and sat on a couch facing Ulysses, who had not moved. "You see," she said to him in her low voice, "in all the years that I have waited for my husband to return from Troy, I have spoken to many travelers." She gestured vaguely with a slender hand. "There have been so many . . . I cannot remember them all. Some of these travelers invented stories, so that I would reward them with a warm cloak or a new tunic. They would claim to have seen Ulysses in some king's palace far from here, or embarking from a seaport, or even sailing toward Ithaca in his ship." She lifted her hand again, and let it fall. "I have listened to so many stories . . . and believed them all."

"Lies!" said the nurse. "Every liar in the world has come here."

"Yes," said Penelope in her soft voice. "I am afraid so. But still I must try to find out."

"You will hear no lies from my lips, O Queen," said Ulysses.

Penelope smiled sadly. Ulysses looked at her face, white and unhappy, and thought: *She has aged, my Penelope.* Then he dropped his eyes to his own bare, dirty feet. *But so have I,* he thought.

The queen saw him glance down, and said quickly, "You must be tired and dusty. Sit now, and Euryclea will bathe your feet, as she used to do for King Ulysses. Then we will talk." She rose and went back to the window.

Euryclea gave an order to one of the maids, and soon a steaming basin of hot water was brought in and set on the floor near Ulysses. The old nurse squatted on a stool before him and pushed up the sleeves of her robe. Ulysses sat with his face drawn back into the shadows. He watched Penelope. From below, from the great hall, came the sounds of heavy feet stamping in time to a drinking song.

The maids bustled about the room, whispering to one another as they worked. Penelope stood motionless at the window, her head bowed in the twilight. Euryclea lowered Ulysses' feet into the hot, soothing water. She began to wash his legs. A maid approached with a flaring torch and set it in a wall bracket near them.

A sudden loud gasp came from Euryclea, and there was a clangor as the bronze basin almost overturned on the marble floor. Ulysses looked down. The old nurse was staring up at his face excitedly. Her fingers rested on his leg, on the long boar scar that now gleamed whitely in the torchlight. Euryclea's old face was alive with joy. She opened her lips to speak.

Ulysses leaned forward swiftly and clapped his hand over her mouth. He looked to see if any of the maids had noticed. "Old woman," he whispered, his lips close to Euryclea's ear, "if you would have me stay alive, be silent! A hundred enemies are below." He held her tightly for a moment, his eyes darting about the room. But none of the maids had noticed anything. Penelope still gazed out the window. He took his hand away and leaned back into the shadows.

"Not a word to anyone, do you understand?" he murmured, his lips barely moving. The old woman nodded. Then she quickly ducked her head to hide the happy smile that spread over her wrinkled face. She drew a corner of Ulysses' cloak over the scar. As she took his leg again, Ulysses could feel her fingers tremble.

When she was drying her lord's feet with a clean linen cloth, they both suddenly heard a sobbing from where Penelope stood at the window. The old woman dropped the cloth and scurried to her mistress. She folded her arms comfortingly about the weeping queen.

"My child, my treasure," the nurse crooned, leading Penelope to a couch, "calm yourself. It is too soon to give up hope. King Ulysses may come home after all."

Euryclea stroked the queen's shining hair, and over her head gazed steadily at Ulysses. The king in beggar's rags looked back at her, and he looked at the trembling shoulders of his wife, but he did not speak.

Finally Queen Penelope straightened up and dried her eyes. She turned to Ulysses with a sad smile. "Forgive an unhappy woman," she said. "Now—you must tell me what you know about my husband. Did you

The old nurse stared up at him excitedly

see him with your own eyes? Or do you bring me some traveler's tale you have heard?"

"My lady," said Ulysses, his old man's voice wavering like the torch flame high on the wall behind him, "I saw the long-suffering King Ulysses, and he was on his way here. If I were you I would not give up hope. I think you will see your husband again within this very month."

Penelope shook her head slowly from side to side. She stared past Ulysses, out through the dark square of the window toward the sea. She said, "If you only knew how often in the past ten years I have been told that." And she bent her head and began to cry again, softly.

"But now I am not able to wait any longer," she said through her tears. "The men who would marry me are too insistent. I cannot hold them off." She paused to take a sobbing breath, and then said, "Tomorrow I choose a new husband."

"Who will it be?" asked Ulysses.

"Whoever wins the test," she answered. And she explained that often, years ago, her husband the king would test his skill with bow and arrow, in the great hall of the palace. Down the center of the hall, Ulysses would set up twelve Greek axes in a long row, carefully, so that the holes pierced in the blades were in line with each other, and a man could see straight through them to the end of the row. Then Ulysses would take his curved bow, step back a distance, and shoot an arrow through the holes in all twelve ax blades.

"He was a great archer, my husband," said Penelope. "His bow is still here. Only a very strong man can bend it. Whoever does bend it and shoot an arrow through the axes I shall have to marry." And she fell silent.

Finally Ulysses said gently, "Who do you think it will be, my lady?"

Penelope shrugged. "What does it matter? They say Antinous is the strongest. But whoever it will be" —she began to sob again—"whoever takes me as his wife shall never drive the memory of Ulysses from my heart. I will remember him even in my dreams—forever, forever!" She buried her face in her arms.

Ulysses sat for a long moment with his eyes on Penelope's quivering back. Then he turned and beckoned Euryclea to him. "Let her sleep," he whispered. And he rose and went out of the room. He tried not to listen to Penelope's sobs as he went.

"Take pity on her, my lord," whispered Euryclea at the door.

He looked at the old nurse. "Do you think I would not like to?" he asked. "It wrenches my heart to see her thus. But there is danger in the house now, and I must deal with it first."

The old woman sighed. "Yes, the suitors would look at her face and know you had returned."

Ulysses nodded. "Now you understand," he said.

"Come, make a bed for me in the hall. I think our guests have all left for the night. They must be looking forward to tomorrow."

The sound of Penelope's weeping seemed to fill his ears as he followed the old woman down the dark steps of his palace.

XIV

The Twelve Axes

"Father," said Telemachus, squinting in the morning sunshine at the palace door, "I know you are a great warrior. For ten years now the minstrels have been singing of your deeds at Troy, and of your courage in battle. But you are a man, not a god, and there are more than a hundred against us!"

Ulysses smiled calmly. "Perhaps a god will help us," he said. "We will pray, Telemachus. But whether a god comes or not we still have our strong arms and our wits. I have triumphed before over my enemies," said the wily king of the Ithacans, the conqueror of Troy, "and I will triumph again."

He laughed at his son's worried face. "Come," he said, "it will be a good day. Look how the sun shines!"

"The sun always shines in Ithaca, Father," said the prince gloomily.

"In Ithaca, yes," said Ulysses, "but not in the places I have been. When I see it now, for the first time in ten years of wandering, I know I have come out of the land of demons at last.

"My boy," he said, squeezing Telemachus' arm in his powerful fingers, "for years I have been facing all manner of monsters on sea and land. But these suitors—they are only ordinary men. What does it matter how many they are?" He scowled, and his grip tightened on his tall son's arm. "They are evil, Telemachus, and the gods will help us punish them. These arrogant men will pay for their wrongdoing, as surely as my poor comrades paid for slaughtering the conquered Trojans. The gods never forget anything, Telemachus—they watch and wait, and never forget."

Ulysses looked around the palace courtyard. The sea wind was warm on his face. "Your mother's eager wooers will be arriving soon," he said. "We must not be seen talking together. Now, everything is ready? You took all the spears and shields down from the walls?"

"Yes, Father. I put them in the armor room. No one saw."

"Good. You and Eumaeus both know the plan? You are certain?"

"We know it, Father."

"Then there is nothing left to do but pray," said Ulysses. "Pray to the goddess Athena, Telemachus. She always helped me when I was sore beset at Troy. I think she will help you become a man today." And he gathered his beggar's cloak, tattered and filthy, about his shoulders and hobbled to the palace threshold.

He was sitting there, an old man sunning himself, when the suitors began to arrive. They sauntered in gaily, proudly, their rich cloaks flapping in the breeze, their bronze swords glittering at their sides. They did not even glance down at the beggar hunched on the floor.

When all one hundred and eight were inside the hall, Eumaeus the swineherd came and closed the great doors. No one noticed that he also locked them.

"Look, Amphimedon, see how bravely little Telemachus sets up his father's axes," jeered Antinous, sipping wine from a double-handled cup of gold.

"Yes," cried Amphimedon, "he looks almost like a man!"

Telemachus flushed darkly, but did not turn from his task. A broad strip of earth, strewn with the ashes of the palace hearth fires, ran through the center of the hall, dividing the marble floor. At the end near the staircase lay a pile of axes, with iron blades and smooth olive-wood handles. Telemachus was carefully setting them upright in a long row, planting their shafts in a narrow trench he had dug. He worked slowly, stamping down the earth around every ax handle.

When he had finished, he went back to the other end of the hall, near where the old beggar sat leaning against the doorpost. The prince dropped to one knee and squinted at the axes. Each iron ax blade had a small round hole pierced in it, and as Telemachus looked down the row he saw that he had done a good job. The holes were all in line; he could see straight through the twelve iron axes to the far end of the hall.

Prince Telemachus rose to his feet and dusted off his hands. He looked about the hall slowly. The lordly wooers were having a fine time; they ate and drank and sang as merrily as ever they had in all their three years of feasting in Ulysses' palace.

Far down the hall, near the inner staircase, old Euryclea stood watching the prince. He nodded to her. The nurse turned and climbed the steps to the upper rooms of the palace. She went through the door at the top of the stairs and closed it behind her firmly.

Telemachus glanced at the swineherd Eumaeus, who stood leaning against the narrow door of a side passage that led to the armor room. Telemachus also let his eyes rest for a moment on the old beggar at the threshold. Then the young prince took a deep breath and raised both his hands high.

"It is time!" he called. "Swineherd, bring the bow!"

Eumaeus stooped, and lifted a heavy, unstrung bow from the floor at his feet. He came forward and handed the bow to Telemachus. He slipped a polished leather quiver, bristling with feathered arrows, from his shoulder and set it on the floor. Then he went back to the little door behind the marble pillars.

With both hands Telemachus lifted the great bow over his head. Curving, massive, it gleamed in the air like the powerful arm of a god. From one tip of polished oxhorn the bowstring dangled loosely.

"Who shall try to string it first?" the young prince demanded. "Who thinks he can bend the bow and stretch the sinew across it? Who thinks himself strong enough?"

As the question echoed in the hall, Amphimedon laughed loudly. "Do not shout at us, little boy," he said, "or we will send you up to your mother. Be quiet, and you will soon see what men can do."

Telemachus looked at him coldly. "Here, braggart," he said. "Try."

Amphimedon leaped to his feet in anger. He started forward, gripping his sword hilt, but Antinous, tall and burly, threw out an arm and pushed him aside. The broad-shouldered giant rose from his chair, wiping his wine-stained mouth with his fist. He strode forward and took the bow.

Setting one curved end on the marble floor, he put his sandaled foot on it heavily. Then he wrapped both massive hands about the upper end, from which the bowstring of sinew hung. He took a deep breath and began to pull downward.

Telemachus watched him. The swineherd Eumaeus watched him, from the shadows by the armor-room door. Amphimedon and all the other suitors watched, motionless and silent. The only sound in the great hall was that of Antinous' rasping breath as he strained at the bow.

His knuckles grew white, and he bared his teeth in a grimace of effort and pain. His face grew red, and then purple; his knuckles cracked loudly. He grunted and took a firmer hold, and tried again. The muscles quivered in his arms. Perspiration gleamed on his forehead.

He could not string the bow. He straightened up with a gasp and flung it down, clattering, at Telemachus' feet. Without a word he stamped back to his table and his wine goblet.

"Well, braggart?" called Telemachus, holding the bow toward Amphimedon. "Perhaps your friend Antinous has drunk too much wine."

Amphimedon snatched the bow from him and spat on the marble floor. The hall fell quiet again as he tried to string the heavy weapon of death. He groaned through clenched teeth, and he heaved and strained, but the bow of King Ulysses remained unstrung.

And after Amphimedon had given up, glowering, many others tried. They came forward swaggering or scowling or blustering; they came forward arrogantly or nervously; but no matter how they came, or how long or how hard they tried, they could not string the bow.

When the last lordly wooer had given up, Antinous rose to his feet. He was smiling with relief, and he said, "You see? The gods are against us. We should never have picked this day—it is clearly a day not good for the stringing of bows. Tomorrow let us try again. Let the axes stand. We will shoot through them yet." He raised his drinking cup. "Now let us be merry again!"

And so they were. They poured more wine, and Amphimedon and another suitor, Eurymachus, struck up a song. They sang gaily, noisily; they sang of how tomorrow would be a better day. Antinous grinned, and kept time with his goblet on the table-top.

"Hear me, young noblemen," rang out a voice, high and wavering. "Hear me, O glorious wooers of the queen."

The singers paused. It was the old beggar who had spoken, from where he sat on the marble threshold.

"What do you want, old fool?" said Eurymachus sharply.

"Godlike sir," said the beggar, "I would like to try the bow, please. Let me see if there is some strength left in these arms."

In the midst of the roaring laughter that followed, Antinous shouted, "You overstep yourself, beggar! Be content that we let you sit here among your betters. Now be quiet, or you will be sorry!" He went back to his wine, and the singers, when they had laughed their fill, went back to their gay song.

The beggar fitted the shaft to the great bow, drew the

But Eumaeus the swineherd quietly handed the curved bow to the beggar and leaned the quiver of arrows against the doorpost. The suitors were too busy to notice as the old man sitting on the floor turned the heavy bow over in his hands, this way and that, as though examining it for scratches or signs of age.

But some of the suitors heard the sudden twang of the bowstring.

They stared, unbelieving. The tattered beggar had strung the bow. He had strung it as easily as a shepherd stretches the rawhide trigger of a snare to trap the wild jackals who menace his sheep.

bowstring back to his chest, and let fly the sharp arrow

The beggar twanged the sinew once again, loudly, still without rising from the threshold. And then he fitted a notched arrow to the string, drew it back to his chest, and shot it through the twelve axes.

The bronze-tipped arrow clanged noisily against the marble steps beyond the last upright ax.

The echoes were still ringing in the hall as Ulysses sprang to his feet and shook himself free of the ragged cloak. He seized the leather quiver and spilled its arrows out on the floor beside him. Then he fitted another shaft to the great bow.

When he spoke again it was in no beggar's voice. It was in the ringing voice of Ulysses the king of

Ithaca, home in his palace at last. He said, "It is time to give our noble guests their supper, Telemachus, while yet there is light." And he drew the bowstring, and let fly the sharp arrow.

Antinous, motionless with surprise, sat with his head turned toward the doorway and his drinking cup poised in mid-air. The arrow struck him in the throat. Blood gushed from his mouth and nostrils, and he pitched forward on his face. The mists of death closed about him, and the golden goblet clattered far out onto the marble floor.

A wild uproar filled the hall as the suitors scrambled to their feet, overturning chairs and tables and cups of dark wine. The noble suitors sprang to the walls, but the spears and shields that had hung there yesterday were gone now, locked in the armor room by Telemachus.

"Pray!" rang out Ulysses' voice. "Pray now to the gods you have ignored!" He hooked another bronze-pointed arrow to his bow and slowly drew it back.

"It is King Ulysses!" said Eurymachus, and he stepped forward, hands held out. "Noble king," he said, "it was Antinous who led us here. He is dead now, and you are avenged, so put away your arrows. Let us be friends—we will pay you back for everything we have consumed."

But Ulysses shook his head. "No," he said. "You have dishonored my house and flouted the gods, because you thought I should never more return from Troy. But I am home now."

"Spare us, O King," pleaded Eurymachus, coming closer. Then suddenly he whipped out his sharp sword and sprang at Ulysses.

The bowstring twanged, and the arrow caught Eurymachus in the chest, just over the heart. His sword clanged loudly on the marble as he died. Leaping over the body came Amphimedon now, swinging his razor-edged sword as Ulysses bent for another arrow.

"There!" cried Amphimedon, but the cry became a death gasp as he ran upon the gleaming point of Telemachus' spear.

The tall prince stood beside his father now, eager for battle, his eyes burning. From the side door behind the pillars Eumaeus hurried toward them, carrying an armful of spears. The old swineherd let the weapons crash to the floor, and then with a fierce cry he snatched one up and hurled it at a suitor.

The wooers seized chairs and tables and used them as shields. Brandishing their swords, they charged forward at the little group by the door. But one by one they met death. Here a suitor staggered and fell, clutching at the feathered shaft of Ulysses' arrow buried in his chest. There one doubled over, screaming in agony, as Telemachus' spear caught him in the stomach. Blood mixed with spilt wine upon the marble floor. Corpses lay everywhere.

Some of the suitors managed to get spears and shields from a back storeroom. They rushed forward, only to be cut down by Ulysses' arrows. They stood back and hurled the spears; sharp-eyed Telemachus deflected them with his heavy shield.

Ulysses killed a suitor with his last arrow, dropped the bow, and picked up a long-shafted spear. The suitors dashed forward grimly, desperately. But the spears of Ulysses and Telemachus and Eumaeus did not waver. Screams rose up to the shadowy rafters, and the marble hall ran with blood.

At last not a suitor was alive. Ulysses stepped forward slowly into the middle of the silent hall. He let his bronze spear fall to the marble and stood looking about as the echoes rang.

Now the door at the head of the stairs opened, and old Euryclea crept forth. She hurried down the steps, cackling with joy. Ulysses slowly focused his eyes on her.

"Quiet, woman," he said sternly. "It is shameful to rejoice over slain men. That is what my companions did at Troy, and the gods punished them. Respect the gods, old woman."

He looked at the dead bodies that choked the hall. "It was the gods who slew these men," he said to Telemachus, "the angry gods guiding our hands. Now it is over. Let there be an end to killing."

And he walked toward the steps that led to the upper palace, and Penelope.

At first she could hardly believe him, even when he showed her the white tusk-scar above his knee. But

Ulysses was patient. He sat with his faithful Penelope for a long while, and spoke softly to her of things that only they two could know.

And when he spoke to her of the bed he had built for himself long ago, the bed that had for one post a living olive tree that came up through a hole in the stone floor of the palace, she finally knew this was Ulysses. With a burst of tears, she flung her arms about his neck.

Ulysses shed tears too. And he wept again later when he embraced his old father and brought joy to Laertes' sorrowing heart. Penelope and Laertes, Telemachus and the weary, long-suffering Ulysses shed many tears together that day, tears of happiness.

The brave Ulysses, the man of many wiles, had returned in the twentieth year to his native land, and his trials were at last over.

Epilogue

THE PROPHECY

Once on his travels Ulysses went to consult the blind prophet Teiresias, greatest of the soothsayers. The hero asked about the day of his death, and the blind seer Teiresias made this prophecy:

"Death shall come to thee far from the sea, a death most gentle, that shall lay thee low when thou art overcome with sleek old age, and thy people dwell in prosperity around thee."

There is in Ithaca a mountain clothed with green forests. It is called Mount Neriton, and sailors far out on the sea know its shape and use it as a landmark. King Ulysses' marble palace stood at its foot. One dark night, many years after he had come home, Ulysses rose from sleep in the palace. His hair and beard were white now, and his great strength had left him at last. He was an old man.

All was silent in the palace, but the words of the blind seer's prophecy sounded in Ulysses' ears. He went quietly out into the night, a cloak about his shoulders and in his hand the ashen spear, now old and scarred, that he had used as a boy in the boar hunt on Mount Parnassus so long ago. He climbed up Mount Neriton slowly, using the spear as a staff, plunging its butt spike into the ground at every step. He climbed all night, and when the first light came he was sitting halfway up the slope of Neriton, gazing down at his kingdom.

Dawn with its rosy fingers began to light the world, and Ulysses looked about him. He looked at the white houses and green fields of Ithaca and at the foaming surf that broke on the shore. He looked at the gray sea, restless, vast, cruel—the home of his ancient enemy, Poseidon. He looked toward Troy.

The air grew brighter. Dawn had almost reached Ithaca. Ulysses gripped the shaft of the old spear and turned toward Mount Olympus, home of the gods. He spoke aloud.

"Come, Death," Ulysses said. "Come—I will not try to outwit you this time."

He smiled a little, and closed his eyes, and waited.

Afterword

All this took place in the far, dim past, so long ago that we have no written records of happenings then. But we do have a great many legends and stories about Ulysses and other great heroes—tales that were passed along by word of mouth in the days before men had learned the art of writing.

Four or five centuries after Ulysses, a Greek poet named Homer—some say he was a blind minstrel—collected many of these legends and put them in two long, remarkable poems called the *Iliad* and the *Odyssey*. The *Iliad* tells the story of some incidents in the Trojan War, that long struggle between Greeks and Trojans on the shore of Asia. Ulysses is an important character in the *Iliad;*

but the *Odyssey* is named after him (his older Greek name is Odysseus) and is his special story. The *Odyssey* tells of his long, adventureful journey home from Troy after the fall of that city, and of what he found when he finally reached his home island of Ithaca.

Homer is a mysterious figure; we know almost nothing about him. We do not even know whether "Homer" was one man, or two, or many men—but it does not matter, really, for the poems can stand by themselves. They contain some of the finest poetry and most wonderfully exciting adventures ever written, and they have been enjoyed and admired for nearly thirty centuries.

It is important to understand that Homer, in making his poems about the Trojan War and the wanderings of the resourceful Ulysses, was telling about things that had happened many hundreds of years earlier. And he had no written history to refer to, only word-of-mouth tales and legends. It is as though someone today were to try to write about Christopher Columbus and his discoveries with no history books to help him. As he went about, listening to whatever tales people could tell him about the great admiral who lived five hundred years ago, he might soon have a marvelous, perhaps almost magical, legendary picture of Columbus—a picture that would probably become more remarkable and more heroic with every telling. And before long the actual events behind the legends about the brave explorer Christopher Columbus would be hopelessly buried.

So it was when Homer composed his poems. The legends said that many centuries earlier there had lived a race of heroes who were more powerful and more fearless than ordinary men, and even conversed with the gods (or at least acted as though they did). Homer took these legends at their face value, and so in his *Iliad* and *Odyssey* we can read about gods coming down to earth to help or hinder the heroes, and about men doing superhuman deeds and finding themselves in magical situations.

These are legends. But Homer knew also that his heroes had been living, breathing human beings. He performed his own literary magic, and was able to create characters —Ulysses, Agamemnon, Diomedes—who could do the tremendous deeds that the legends about them required, but at the same time could be recognized as real, believable people. They were, in fact, just like the people, good or bad, of Homer's own day—or of today. Even the powerful gods that flit through Homer's poems, while they can do many things, cannot make a man act in a way that contradicts his own nature. Homer was wise enough to know that a hero who called upon some god to help him was also really calling upon his own inner resources as well. So when Ulysses asks Zeus or Athena to give him the courage to meet some great danger, he is also calling upon himself to summon up all the courage he has within him.

This was Homer's great message—that a god can exist outside men only if he first exists *inside*. Or, to put it another way, men get the gods they deserve.

And when, centuries afterward, the minstrels plucked their lyres and chanted of the trials of long-suffering Ulysses, far from his home, their listeners knew that Homer was giving them this message. But most of all they just sat back and enjoyed the marvelous adventures of one of their favorite friends—the brave and clever Ulysses.

But it happens that Homer does not tell the whole story of Ulysses' life in the two poems. There were many tales about the resourceful red-haired man that Homer did not use; and many legends about Ulysses were born after Homer had died. So, although this book about Ulysses takes its facts mostly from Homer, it also uses legends that cannot be found in the *Iliad* and the *Odyssey*.

After Homer's time, for example, a poet named Stasinus of Cyprus wrote down, in a poem called the *Cypria*, some legends about the Trojan War which Homer had not used. And Arctinus of Miletus, in his *Sack of Ilion*, told of some other legends that do not appear in either of Homer's great poems. These works, and many others like them, have been lost for more than a thousand years. But fifteen centuries ago, when they could still be read, a poet named Quintus Smyrnaeus used the legends they contained to write his own poem about the destruction of King Priam's mighty citadel at Troy. And, after him, other writers used other legends about Ulysses and his exploits. It seems that men will forever be fascinated by the story of the quick-witted wanderer from Ithaca.

The Greek Gods

Of all the gods worshipped by the ancient Greeks, twelve were deemed more important than any others.

ZEUS (called JUPITER in later ages, after the Greeks) was the supreme ruler over heaven, and over all gods and all men. In his mighty wrath, Zeus could hurl flaming thunderbolts upon earth or sea.

HERA (in later ages called JUNO) was the wife of Zeus. Hera was the goddess of marriage, and of motherhood.

POSEIDON (in later ages called NEPTUNE) was the brother of Zeus. He was the god of the sea, and of horses. Earthquakes came from Poseidon, as well as terrible sea storms.

ATHENA (in later ages called MINERVA) was one of the

daughters of Zeus. Athena was the goddess of wisdom and all the peaceful arts, but she was also the goddess of skill in battle.

HERMES (in later ages called MERCURY) was the messenger of the gods. He was the god of eloquence and wit, of travelers, and of herdsmen. Hermes was known for his friendliness to mortals.

ARES (in later ages called MARS) was the fierce god of war.

APOLLO (in later ages still called APOLLO) was the archer-god, the god of prophecy, and the god of song and music. Soothsayers and minstrels were sacred to Apollo.

APHRODITE (in later ages called VENUS) was the goddess of love and of beauty.

HEPHAESTUS (in later ages called VULCAN) was the god of blacksmiths and of all artists and craftsmen.

ARTEMIS (in later ages called DIANA) was the goddess of hunting and of little children.

DEMETER (in later ages called CERES) was the goddess of the harvest and of farming.

HESTIA (in later ages called VESTA) was the goddess of the hearth-fire and of the family.

In addition to these twelve, there were many other less important gods and goddesses. They were found everywhere. Some of them, like the sun-god, Helios, traveled far and wide over the world. Others, like the goddess Calypso, never moved from their own islands or mountains. But every god was far more powerful than any mortal man. The Greeks feared and worshipped them all.

Glossary

Aeolus, EE-o-lus
Agamemnon, ag-a-MEM-non
Alcinous, al-SIN-o-us
Amphimedon, am-FIM-e-don
Antinous, an-TIN-o-us
Aphrodite, af-ro-DIE-tee
Ares, AIR-eez
Arete, a-REE-tee
Athena, a-THEE-na
Autolycus, aw-TOL-i-kus
Charybdis, ka-RIB-dis
Circe, SIR-see
Demodocus, de-MOD-o-kus
Diomedes, die-o-MEE-deez
Elpenor, EL-pen-or
Eumaeus, you-MEE-us
Eurybates, you-RIB-a-teez
Euryclea, you-RIK-lee-a
Eurylochus, you-RILL-o-kus
Eurymachus, you-RIM-a-kus
Hades, HAY-deez
Hermes, HER-meez
Ithaca, ITH-a-ka
Laertes, lay-ERR-teez
Laestrygones, LESS-tri-gohnz
Menelaus, men-e-LAY-us
Mycenae, MY-sen-ee
Nausicaa, naw-si-KAY-a
Neoptolemus, nee-op-TOL-e-mus
Penelope, pe-NEL-o-pee
Phaeacia, fee-AY-sha
Polites, po-LIGHT-eez
Polyphemus, polly-FEE-mus
Poseidon, po-SIGH-don
Scaean, SKEE-an
Scylla, SILL-a
Teiresias, tie-REE-se-us
Telemachus, te-LEM-a-kus
Ulysses, you-LISS-eez
Zeus, zooss

Index

LANDMARK BOOKS

1 The Voyages of Christopher Columbus
2 The Landing of the Pilgrims
3 Pocahontas and Captain John Smith
4 Paul Revere and the Minute Men
5 Our Independence and the Constitution
6 The California Gold Rush
7 The Pony Express
8 Lee and Grant at Appomattox
9 The Building of the First Transcontinental Railroad
10 The Wright Brothers
11 Prehistoric America
12 The Vikings
13 The Santa Fe Trail
14 The Story of the U.S. Marines
15 The Lewis and Clark Expedition
16 The Monitor and the Merrimac
17 The Explorations of Pere Marquette
18 The Panama Canal
19 The Pirate LaFitte and the Battle of New Orleans
20 Custer's Last Stand
21 Daniel Boone
22 Clipper Ship Days
23 Gettysburg
24 The Louisiana Purchase
25 Wild Bill Hickock Tames the West
26 Betsy Ross and the Flag
27 The Conquest of the North and South Poles
28 Ben Franklin of Old Philadelphia
29 Trappers and Traders of the Far West
30 Mr. Bell Invents the Telephone
31 The Barbary Pirates
32 Sam Houston, the Tallest Texan
33 The Winter at Valley Forge
34 The Erie Canal
35 Thirty Seconds Over Tokyo
36 Thomas Jefferson, Father of Democracy
37 The Coming of the Mormons
38 George Washington Carver
39 John Paul Jones, Fighting Sailor
40 The First Overland Mail
41 Teddy Roosevelt and the Rough Riders
42 To California by Covered Wagon
43 Peter Stuyvesant of Old New York
44 Lincoln and Douglas: The Years of Decision
45 Robert Fulton and the Steamboat
46 The F.B.I.
47 Dolly Madison
48 John James Audubon
49 Hawaii, Gem of the Pacific
50 War Chief of the Seminoles
51 Old Ironsides: The Fighting *Constitution*
52 The Mississippi Bubble
53 Kit Carson and the Wild Frontier
54 Robert E. Lee and the Road of Honor
55 Guadalcanal Diary
56 Commodore Perry and the Opening of Japan
57 Davy Crockett
58 Clara Barton, Founder of the American Red Cross
59 The Story of San Francisco
60 Up the Trail from Texas
61 Abe Lincoln: Log Cabin to White House
62 The Story of D-Day: June 6, 1944
63 Rogers' Rangers and the French and Indian War
64 The World's Greatest Showman: The Life of P. T. Barnum
65 Sequoyah: Leader of the Cherokees
66 Ethan Allen and the Green Mountain Boys
67 Wyatt Earp: U.S. Marshal
68 The Early Days of Automobiles
69 The Witchcraft of Salem Village
70 The West Point Story
71 George Washington: Frontier Colonel
72 The Texas Rangers

73 Buffalo Bill's Great Wild West Show
74 Evangeline and the Acadians
75 The Story of the Secret Service
76 Tippecanoe and Tyler Too!
77 America's First World War: General Pershing and the Yanks
78 The Doctors Who Conquered Yellow Fever
79 Remember the Alamo!
80 Andrew Carnegie and the Age of Steel
81 Geronimo: Wolf of the Warpath
82 The Story of the Paratroops
83 The American Revolution
84 The Story of the Naval Academy
85 Alexander Hamilton and Aaron Bur
86 Stonewall Jackson
87 The Battle for the Atlantic
88 The First Transatlantic Cable
89 The Story of the U.S. Air Force
90 The Swamp Fox of the Revolution
91 Heroines of the Early West
92 The Alaska Gold Rush
93 The Golden Age of Railroads
94 From Pearl Harbor to Okinawa

WORLD LANDMARK BOOKS

W-1 The First Men in the World
W-2 Alexander the Great
W-3 Adventures and Discoveries of Marco Polo
W-4 Joan of Arc
W-5 King Arthur and His Knights
W-6 Mary, Queen of Scots
W-7 Napoleon and the Battle of Waterloo
W-8 Royal Canadian Mounted Police
W-9 The Man Who Changed China: The Story of Sun Yat-Sen
W-10 The Battle of Britain
W-11 The Crusades
W-12 Genghis Khan and the Mongol Horde
W-13 Queen Elizabeth and the Spanish Armada
W-14 Simon Bolivar, the Great Liberator
W-15 The Slave Who Freed Haiti: The Story of Toussaint Louverture
W-16 The Story of Scotland Yard
W-17 The Life of St. Patrick
W-18 The Exploits of Xenophon
W-19 Captain Cook Explores the South Seas
W-20 Marie Antoinette
W-21 Will Shakespeare and the Globe Theater
W-22 The French Foreign Legion
W-23 Martin Luther
W-24 The Hudson's Bay Company
W-25 Balboa: Swordsman and Conquistador
W-26 The Magna Charta
W-27 Leonardo Da Vinci
W-28 General Brock and Niagara Fall
W-29 Catherine the Great
W-30 The Fall of Constantinople
W-31 Ferdinand Magellan: Master Mariner
W-32 Garibaldi: Father of Modern Ita
W-33 The Story of Albert Schweitzer
W-34 The Marquis de Lafayette: Bright Sword for Freedom
W-35 Famous Pirates of the New Wor
W-36 Exploring the Himalaya
W-37 Queen Victoria
W-38 The Flight and Adventures of Charles II
W-39 Chief of the Cossacks
W-40 The Adventures of Ulysses
W-41 William the Conqueror
W-42 Jesus of Nazareth
W-43 Julius Caesar
W-44 The Story of Australia
W-45 Captain Cortés Conquers Mexi
W-46 Florence Nightingale

WORLD
Landmark
BOOKS